...wherever you want beauty to touch your life.

When I look out into the universe,
I see order–order caused by intelligence.

Whenever I fly into a new city, and the plane descends,
I look out on the landscape.
I see industry . . . buildings, vehicles, things happening
—the result of intelligence—people in action.

I read once that if you put all the parts to an airplane
in a hanger and leave them,
you would never expect these parts
to assemble themselves into a plane.
Yet that's what some people willingly believe happens
in the creation of earth and man.
That this world, galaxies, universes were created by happenstance
. . . without intelligent thought.

That concept defies reason.

I believe in God, the highest source of intelligent thought.
I believe that the order of the universe is secured
by immutable governing laws.
That light, truth, intelligence and life are somehow synonymous.
That life, light and love are the great motivators.

My work in color was to discover
if immutable laws of color exist
that would govern our personal beauty.

This book is about that quest and the answers I found.

Marilyn Starr Harris

UNLOCKING YOUR BEAUTY CODE

Become
More Beautiful
Than You Ever Imagined
Using Secrets of Beauty
Unlocked by Da Vinci and Newton

Unlocking Your Beauty Code™
Marilyn Starr Harris

Address inquiries to:
The Beauty Code
51 West Center, Ste 426
Orem, UT 84058
877-870-1616
801-226-0616

www.mybeautycode.com
email: info@mybeautycode.com

First published in 2011 by Beauty Innovations, LLC
All rights reserved.

Printed in China by Global PSD
www.globalpsd.com

Library of Congress Cataloging-in-Publication Data available
LCN: 2010904535

ISBN 978-0-9840932-0-5

Cover and book design by Anthony Orme, Julia Nuttall, Marie Zamora, and Linda Maloy
Hair and makeup by Renaissance Beauty Academy, Marilyn Starr Harris and Sara Cameron
Fashion photography by Steve May, Rick Nye, Shaun Knapp and Mary Ann McCullom

Trademarks of Beauty Innovations, LLC.
Beauty Code™, www.mybeautycode.com™,
The Science of Personal Color™,

A portion of the proceeds of this book will go to Lighthouse Lodge Living, a Center for Single Women with children, raised in drug environments. To learn about this organization, go to LightHouseLodgeLiving.org.

The following statements from nationally recognized science, beauty, and marketing experts indicate the degree of sophistication and acceptance of Marilyn Starr Harris's concepts, and products.

Ever since men and women have experienced in their lives the beauty and good harmony of alluring personal color, talented artisans have strived to understand and master the power and energy of color in human feelings. Gifted masters of color, great artists, have left their works and have sometimes expressed their expertise and wisdom. Their genius and sensitivity to color has been an object of study for centuries. The colors used by Leonardo da Vinci in his Mona Lisa are still studied by art scholars.

"Marilyn Starr Harris has mastered this wisdom, applied it in actual practice and can deliver its advantages to her clients; she has a surety of process validated by the laws of physics and by studies of human color perception."

Dr. Robert A. Schluter, PhD
Professor of Physics (retired) MIT and Northwestern University

Northwestern University, College of Arts and Sciences, and Graduate School, Professor of Physics and Astronomy 1961-1992. Emeritus 1992- present; with 120 published research papers and portions of three books arising from experimental research in nuclear physics and elementary particle physics 1947-1988 carried out at University of Chicago, Massachusetts Institute of Technology, Fermi National Accelerator Laboratory, Argonne National Laboratory, Brookhaven National Laboratory, Princeton-Penn Accelerator, and University of California Lawrence Radiation Laboratory.

1988 - 1996, research in theoretical hydrodynamics, supported by NASA since 1993.

Guest appointment: Aspen Institute for Humanities 1967.

Chairman, Radiation Safety Committee, Northwestern University and Medical School, 1980-86.

Faculty, Massachusetts Institute of Technology and Laboratory of Nuclear Science, 1955-1960. Guest Scientist, Brookhaven National Laboratory and Lawrence Radiation Laboratory of the University of California.

World War II, U. S. Army, 1943-46, Manhattan Project, Los Alamos, New Mexico 1944-1946.

PhD, University of Chicago, 1954.

Who's Who in the World, 18th edn.

Who's Who in Science and Engineering, 1972-present

American Physical Society

Sigma Xi Honorary Research Society

National Association of Scholars

professional endorsements

"In reviewing the approach to color presented by Marilyn Starr Harris, I find her materials and concept light years ahead of what is currently available or even on the drawing board in the beauty industry.

"This industry is in dire need of accurate color technology, specifically in the areas of cosmetics, hair color and clothing. Most beauty experts recognize this need.

"Marilyn Starr Harris has combined significant knowledge into concise and precise quality products. The people in the industry today are far less knowledgeable than Marilyn. Both people in the industry and consumers alike want to know how to use color correctly.

"The media tells us incessantly that our appearance makes or breaks us – right down to scratching dry scalp. But no one is telling people specifically how to put it all together accurately. That's why Marilyn Starr Harris's program is so revolutionary. It is based on time honored principles of art and color. It is comprehensive, deep but simple. No one else has dealt with the complexity of fashion and made it so simple for the client. And, it works! People using it look stunning. They know it and they know how to achieve it.

"Marilyn's program helps people get more out of life in attitude, outlook and total function – starting with the magic of color. That's great. It will impact every facet of the beauty industry."

Jim Metcalf
Former National Sales Manager, Fabrege, New York
Former Regional Manager, Revlon, West Coast

"Marilyn Starr Harris teaches women the scientific principles behind beauty so that they can choose the perfect outfit, makeup and hairstyle every time. She has your beauty down to a science – a science that works."

Richard Paul Evans
Fifteen time New York Times bestselling author

"Since the properties of color are scientific in nature, they can be measured and defined. They are not subjective but objective. As surely as prisms and rainbows, there is no opinion on how color works. Physics has examined and explained it scientifically. Since Marilyn Starr Harris's color system is based on the science of color, there's no alternate opinion. It is not opinion – ever. It is color law. Any color system different is based on something less therefore incorrect.

"Even though gravity has been around forever, Newton was the first to define it. Thus man was able to use the power of gravity for his purposes. By defining color, something as sure as gravity, Marilyn Starr Harris has made the power of color accessible to each individual.

"Relationships between colors have also been defined and measured. Universal laws of harmony and beauty dictate that the laws of color and balance applied to you will create harmony, beauty and balance for you." No one in history since has pulled the science behind color and style law together and applied it to makeup, hair and clothing. Marilyn has defined and developed them into a system of appearance you can use to be beautiful.

"Marilyn has done years of research and study on the principles of color and light in both the artistic and scientific worlds in order to lay a solid, scientific basis for her color system. She has then taken all that data and compiled it into a simple, easy to understand and use system that consumers can apply with total confidence in all their color decisions.

"It's like using a car. You get in, turn the key, put it in gear, step on the gas, and it goes. With little or no understanding on your part of the mechanics and dynamics of the car, you can still enjoy all the benefits of that marvelous invention. Likewise with The Beauty Code™ and The Science of Personal Color™ System, you can enjoy all the benefits of a complete, trusted and tested color system by simply following the basic directions. The system automatically does all the work for you."

Richard Gadd
Founder: Kiddie Kandids

professional endorsements

Bach and The Beauty Code

"Johann Sebastian Bach was the first to explain the principles of why some music sounded harmonious and other music discordant. People of his day didn't understand principles of music. Bach identified and developed the system which explained the different harmonies that makes music pleasing, inspiring and exciting—even fun. Thus he freed people to compose myriads of music with confidence. Marilyn Starr Harris has done this with color.

"In music, the pitch and desired tone can be difficult to achieve without supervision and guidance; music must have melodic flow and blending to create balance. Just as in music, Marilyn Starr Harris has created a color system based on color law which creates harmony and balance for people. With the guidance of her system, individuals can have a feeling of security and knowledge in creating complimentary effects in their appearance and decor. Using correct laws of color and style, people can radiate their inner beauty."

Tonya Stimpson
Bachelor of Music Performance and Pedagogy
Master of Music Performance and Pedagogy
Concert Pianist; Piano Performance Competitions Judge
Member: MTNA, Encore, UFMA, AIM

"Through the scientific principles Marilyn Starr Harris has discovered, I believe her book, Unlocking Your Beauty Code™ will become #1 in beauty instruction and the only book with the science to back it up. Marilyn's program is amazing."

Robert G. Allen
New York Times bestselling author of Nothing Down.

"I find Marilyn Starr Harris's research and concepts to be the only truly original idea I've seen in the beauty industry since I came to America in 1962."

Franz Pum, PhD
Cosmetic Chemist for Clairol, Redken, Revlon, Sebastian, Alberto-Culver

"By her years of working one-on-one with clients and her study of skin-compatible ingredients, Marilyn Starr Harris has broken barriers in providing consumers with safe and beneficial products for years to come. Her color concept is the answer to questions that have plagued the hair color business for years."

Harry Robins
Director of Marketing, Rayette Corporation
Consultant for Revlon, Summit Lab, Christine Valmy, Redken, LeMar

"The whole trend of color is confusing because no one has put their finger on the basis of the principle governed by color law that applies to color typing people—until now.

"The color system presented by Marilyn Starr Harris is based on color law as old as the earth itself with answers that experts worldwide have searched for and never found."

Bob Gervitch
Revlon Vice President Marketing, Western Division USA

UNLOCKING YOUR BEAUTY CODE

Featuring

The
Science
of
Personal Color

SPC System by Marilyn Starr Harris

contents

You Want More Than PRETTY

IMAGINE . . .

> . . . always turning out a radiant presence in your appearance.

> . . . knowing how you can always look beautiful.

> . . . looking vibrant and naturally beautiful any time, in any activity and at any age.

> . . . knowing how to combine your most becoming colors for a highly attractive wardrobe, radiant makeup, and stylish hair.

IMAGINE . . . HAVING KNOWLEDGE THAT GIVES YOU CONTROL

> . . . knowing how to choose and use colors to electrify your appearance, even in quiet ways.

> . . . knowing color so well that you can use your "less-than-perfect" colors beautifully anytime you need or want to.

> . . . looking ideally proportioned by choosing those styles that bring the different parts of your body into balance.

> . . . having a perfect understanding of color and style so you could use both with confidence and creativity.

> . . . having total control of your appearance.

IMAGINE . . . KNOWING HOW TO SAVE AND SPEND YOUR MONEY WISELY

> . . . never wasting money when you purchase anything involving color, style and personality whether it's for you, your spouse, your family, your friends, your home or your yard.

IMAGINE . . . A CLOSET THAT WORKS FOR YOU, NOT AGAINST YOU

> . . . going to your closet knowing that no matter what you pick, it will make you look fabulous.

> . . . having a closet where everything always coordinates and works together.

IMAGINE . . . APPLYING YOUR MAKEUP LIKE A PROFESSIONAL

> . . . looking naturally pleasing, not painted, because you wear makeup in your perfect colors.

> . . . applying your makeup in the right patterns to bring your features into ideal balance.

IMAGINE . . . CREATING YOUR SIGNATURE APPEARANCE

> . . . knowing how to create your appearance signature, right down to a toothbrush.

You Want CONFIDENT
You Want CAPABLE

IMAGINE . . . CHOOSING THE RIGHT HAIR STYLE AND HAIR COLOR

- . . . understanding all the perfect shapes for your hairstyles by your total body structure.

- . . . knowing all the options for hairstyles that will make you look terrific in any fashion or style change.

- . . . knowing the secrets of getting hair color you love that looks fabulous on you.

- . . . telling your hairstylist exactly how to accomplish getting hair color you love; knowing how to choose those perfect hair colors "off-the-shelf."

- . . . knowing how to adapt your hairstyle and clothing to whatever mood you may want to express.

IMAGINE . . . DECORATING FOR FULFILLMENT IN YOUR HOME

- . . . having color confidence in creating unusual and pleasing room decor for your living spaces.

- . . . being your own best interior decorator—knowing how to coordinate color, mix and match color, blend and embolden colors.

IMAGINE . . . SHOPPING SMART

- . . . walking through a store—and every store—moving through racks and stacks of clothes, rows and counters of makeup, and knowing instantly if a dress, skirt, top, lip or blush color is right for you.

- . . . being your own best authority on yourself in all your buying decisions.

- . . . directing sales people from your perfect understanding of color and style rather than being dependent on them.

IMAGINE . . . ALL YOUR POSSIBILITIES

- . . . the time, money and energy you will save.
- . . . the compliments you will get.
- . . . the fulfillment you will have from everything you purchase or create.

That is the power of the system you hold in your hands.
The science guarantees it.

*Imagine having **complete color** and **style confidence***

Unlocking Your Beauty Code™

The Discovery of

The knowledge in this book comes from principles revealed in the work and research of master artists and scientists over the past several centuries. My contribution has been to carry these discoveries into a new dimension of how they apply to you and all people worldwide who want sure and easy solutions for their appearance. I brought these principles together in The Beauty Code™—a system which unlocks and explains the science of both color and style and makes them useful to you.

TODAY

I have total control and confidence knowing how to choose and use color for terrific looking outfits and naturally beautiful makeup. I know exactly how to create striking home decor and colorful yet tasteful landscaping. My understanding of color, style, and personality as it relates to others and myself gives me enjoyment and confidence. It allows me to have fun and be more creative. Though small, I love my closet and everything in it. I have less clothing but more outfits than ever before because of my knowledge. My biggest problem is letting go of old clothes because I still love them.

When shopping, I know instantly whether an item of clothing will be perfect for me. I know my best blouses are longer blouses with a V-neck and ¾ sleeves. Why? Because I have a wide face and a short, medium wide neck. A V-neckline balances both those features. For that reason, I avoid turtlenecks and I know why I won't wear them. I never waste money on bracelets or large watches. I know exactly why. I have short arms, and medium bone structure so bracelets or noticeable watches make my arms appear shorter. Because I have short legs I avoid bright print or plaid skirts/pants and dropped waistlines. I choose instead simple, straight, cuffless plain colored pants and shoes with one and a half inch heels because they make my legs look longer.

My clients, empowered with this knowledge, enjoy this same control and confidence with their appearance and in their homes. They star in their own show of life. The system empowers them

BUT IT WASN'T ALWAYS SO

In my twenties and thirties, I felt constant anxiety and frustration in how to put my appearance, our home, and our yard together.

Your Beauty Code

In an advanced tailoring class, I spent long hours toiling over an expensive wool coat. I'd bought the highest quality fabric because I thought I would love wearing this coat for years. But only a year later, wearing it made me feel tired and depressed. Horrific guilt surfaced every time I looked at it. I didn't know why. I didn't know how to prevent other clothing mistakes. At the same time, I had a cheap cotton gingham blouse that I wore over and over again—literally until it was threadbare. I remember a print dress of multiple shades of purple. Warned that purple was difficult to wear, I wore that dress until it fell apart. Why had the wool coat failed while the purple dress had won? I didn't know.

I'd buy a lipstick because a makeup consultant told me it was the in color, then I'd regularly pass over it and choose other colors. Why? Regardless of fashion, why was I choosing to wear one lipstick over another, one coat, one eyeshadow, one dress over another? I wanted to know.

I'd buy plants and flowers, then hate what I had created. It all started after the second of my eight children was born. I took a good, long inventory of myself. Plagued with the same self-doubts of most women, I wanted to take my life to a new dimension. In a nutshell, I was confused about me. I wanted to know not only how to look good, but also how to decorate our home and choose distinct clothing for our family members. I wanted a system—a workable plan that I could simply apply to get fulfilling results in these areas of my daily responsibilities. I also wanted to stretch my mind, my interests. I wanted to grow, to expand me.

I appreciated the tasks my life brought me. I was a wife, a lover, a mother, a house-keeper, a homemaker, a breadwinner, a bread maker, a chauffeur, a friend, a sister, a daughter, a gardener, arranger of flowers, and a community volunteer. I played these roles willingly and lovingly. But . . .

I wanted knowledge . . . knowledge about me. Who was Marilyn? Was I anything other than my roles? Separated from those I loved, was I, myself, lovable? Capable? Creative? I was convinced that I already was this person. I just didn't look like this person. I decided, as part of my becoming, to work on a prettier facade. So I enrolled in a regional finishing school. I wanted to appear lovely and poised, I just lacked the necessary skills.

I had never thought of myself as a beautiful person. While my parents taught me to achieve in school and work, they also told me that makeup was unnecessary, even vain. They did not reinforce natural beauty as part of self worth. In fact, both my parents often told me I'd be "a wall flower like my mother." So I, like many others, saw myself as unattractive, therefore unpopular.

Finishing school was fun. I learned how to order meals in French, how to stand and sit like a lady, even how to reduce my thighs and increase the size of my calves.

Find the **information** *you* **you** *need to* **complete yourself**

But when I finished the course, I still couldn't go into a department store and confidently buy clothes and makeup that I knew complemented me. I knew how to act but not how to look. This frustrated me.

Beauty commands so much importance in our society. I was trying to understand how to better present myself, but all the tricks and gimmicks—the half-answers—irritated me. When someone told me I looked lovely, I genuinely appreciated the compliment but I wasn't certain why I looked good or how or if I could accomplish the same appearance again.

I wanted more than pretty. I wanted confident. I wanted capable. I didn't want to rely on the opinions of others. What became a significant commitment for me—the search to understand color and beauty—began as a simple quest to improve my appearance. I wanted a simple, direct plan to look good—one to make shopping and planning easy. It did not exist. I wanted my look to accurately represent me.

THE RESEARCH BEGINS

Initially, I began to research fashion design and style because I love the artistry of creating a look and I wanted that skill. Later, I continued because, as a consultant to clients, as a buyer of fabrics, cosmetics, and clothes, I needed to know how to buy for and please customers. When businesses don't sell merchandise, profit is eaten up or lost. Products don't sell because customers don't like them. Why? I wanted to know.

I began by collecting bits and pieces of information that interested me. Eventually and over 15 years, I compiled several volumes of data as my research drew me deeper into the knowledge of style and health.

About this time I ran into my instructor from the finishing school. I enthusiastically told her about the information I was finding, the fashion and color discoveries that I was making. To my surprise, rather than sharing my excitement about what I was learning, she threatened to sue me if I ever went into competition against her.

My intent at that time was only to find the information I needed to complete myself. Her threatening reaction caught me off guard. It taught me how little I could count on professional help. Her reaction also told me my collections had value.

At that time, I didn't understand the role color plays in beauty but that soon changed with an experience that opened the world of color for me and began my understanding of how color really works.

WHERE TO GO

While attending a self-help seminar, I was fascinated by our instructor's appearance. She exuded an overall confidence, poise, and attractiveness. As I watched her teach the class, however, I began to note that her features were far from perfect. She had irregular teeth, an awkward mouth, even a quite crooked nose. Yet in spite of these physical imperfections, her appearance was warm, inviting–lovely.

Each week I studied her, puzzled over why she appeared so beautiful. At the end of our seminar, she invited us to attend another class, a color class where we could learn our best colors by a new "Seasons" system. As though a light had been turned on in my dark brain, I realized the secret of her attractiveness was in the colors she wore. Her use of color in wardrobe and makeup did not seem remarkable, yet the impact on her appearance was powerful. With color, she controlled her physical limitations and created an radiant appearance.

Confidence without capability is false

Recognizing that color was behind her remarkable, glowing appearance was a gestalt for me. I saw and understood that the proper use of color not only compensates, it creates. Just as what we are adds up to more than the sum of our parts, color multiplies our virtues to enhance our appearance. Our instructor looked good because the colors she wore made her look whole and complete.

MY SEASON OF DISCONTENT

Hoping to find answers in her system of color, I attended her color seminar. I was diagnosed a "Spring." I was given a swatch of color samples and one thing more: confidence that I could accomplish the same control of color that I recognized in my instructor.

I soon discovered, however, that confidence without capability is false. Belief in partial answers or untruths will not give you the results you want. Having seen the difference the Seasons Color System made in the appearance of my instructor, I trusted it. I used it.

Just one problem—the "Season's System" didn't work for me. It never can. The principles behind it are flawed. My "Spring swatches" contained lime-green samples—a color I've never liked. But so what? It didn't matter what I liked. Springs should like colors from the Spring swatch. Who was I to doubt?

The fact that I was placed in a group containing so many colors that I didn't like should have warned me that I had been diagnosed incorrectly. At that time, however, I didn't know enough about color to realize what bad advice I'd received. I went forward on blind faith as did millions of women.

*You want to look **true,** true to **yourself** and your **natural feelings** of **color***

My husband, Robert, and I were in the process of building a new home. I started decorating our house using my color samples. My home, wardrobe and appearance were going to be sensational. So I decorated our new home based on "Spring" colors. Later I felt uncomfortable living with my choices. My house looked and felt drab. I felt drab. I changed my wardrobe. Still feeling "off," I changed my makeup base. I even changed my hair color from its natural ash brown to auburn in my attempt to achieve harmony in my color effects.

I achieved harmony. I received compliments. But I felt cacophony. While I looked good, I looked untrue—untrue to myself, untrue to my natural feelings of color and personality.

I constantly fussed with my look. Other people could compliment me about my appearance but when I looked in the mirror, I didn't see me. I saw a combination of someone else's color perceptions.

ANALYZING COLOR

Since those days, I have been told that I am an "Autumn" or a perfect "Winter." I've been analyzed both Color Key One and Color Key Two. I've been told I should be able to define my color by thinking in terms of a month or a time of day. I've been told I can wear any color if I change my makeup. (I'd already done that and didn't like the results.) I wanted reliable, predictable, and simple.

Many systems of color analysis exist. Over the years, I investigated each new wave of color "discovery" that hit the beauty market. But the story was always incomplete. Nowhere did anyone explain the science of why or how one color looked better. How could I make intelligent suggestions for my client's use of color when the existing theories lacked predictable results?

I needed a precise understanding of color law. I believed in color as a true principle for creating a beautiful appearance because I had seen it at work. Fortunately, my father conducted research in nutrition for a large feed company in Iowa. I learned research methods from him that I needed to investigate this concept further.

I realized at this time that women have to shop. Their role as home and family manager requires it. Besides our own clothing and makeup, we buy clothing and makeup for our family and friends. We have to choose bedding, kitchen and bath linens, furniture, carpet, drapes and more. We buy most of the gifts. Usually we pick and coordinate the flowers in our yard. We give our opinions on the color of our buildings—brick, siding, roofing, and wood. And we choose vehicle colors.

It can be fun to make all these choices. We get teased a lot about our shopping. But think about how much more accomplished we'd be and feel with a system that connected us to our instincts and the instincts of our loved ones in making all these choices.

*The **correct color** for **you** begins with the **science** of how **all things** are **colored***

My studies of existing color systems took more than forty-two months as I traveled across the United States seeking out recognized color experts or reading their materials. Disappointed, I found these systems poorly founded, scientifically incomplete, and arbitrary. I found myself left with many unanswered questions. I wanted information that would give me solutions.

At this point, I put all my existing knowledge of color systems aside. I decided rather than try to work around or reform an existing system, I needed to understand color itself scientifically. I didn't know what I would find. I just knew that no one else had answers. I believed that color law would provide those answers.

In the midst of this investigation, I began to formulate a logical argument—an incomplete syllogism.

First, your correct colors begin with the science of how all things are colored.

Second, the one constant color in each of us, regardless of race, is the color of our skin—more specifically, the proportion of colors that make up our individual skin. These colors are defined by the physical composition of our bodies, which remains the same from birth to death.

Third, if color interacts with other color (and it does), then that interaction is based on physical laws. If I understand those principles, then I will know why one skin color is complimented by one shade of makeup or clothing and made to look unattractive by another.

I knew natural laws govern color. I believed that by understanding those laws, I could purchase and coordinate my wardrobe with confidence. I could base my color decisions on scientific principles.

A reaction happens to us when we place color on us.

Most people, if they think about it at all, consider their color choices as strictly personal preference (like preferring strawberry ice cream to pistachio) or cultural habit ("pink is a more feminine color than red or blue," "Mother always dressed my sister in blue and me in green so we could tell our clothes apart, and I've just stuck with it"), or a reliance on an outside expert ("the clerk says I look good in this color and she must know").

I was seeking something more substantial—a method by which people could bring out the best in their natural features. I discovered. I learned.

My four greatest discoveries from my research were:

1. Sir Isaac Newton's experiments with light. His work gave me a scientific constant for color and a useful color wheel for color typing people. He was the first known to accurately name the primary colors and the first to form the color spectrum (of prisms and rainbows) into a color wheel.

2. The color law of light is the same color law by which our bodies are colored. This color law also correlates with pigment colors with which we color everything we design, manufacture, create, and paint.

3. The Impressionists use of color was influenced by Michel Eugene Chevreul, the Director of Dyes for the Royal Manufactures, who produced tapestries for the French Kings and most of Europe. Chevreul, in placing colored threads against each other in tapestries, learned the laws of how colors, in proximity, relate to each other. This law explains why some colors look better on us than others. Chevreul explained the reaction that happens to us when we place color on us in cosmetics, clothes, and hair color.

4. The meticulously detailed studies of Leonardo da Vinci on the ratios of the human body parts, one to another. This fueled the idea of how to use design

in clothing, makeup patterns, and hair styles to give people the appearance of being ideally proportioned.

With these four discoveries, I created The Beauty Code™, a system that discovers your best colors and styles.

PROFESSIONAL

During the next six years, my husband and I operated three fabric stores; we offered custom wardrobe design and tailoring for our clients. Daily, I met the challenge of helping my clients achieve their best appearance. As a buyer, I now had a "material" reason to understand color. In the middle of researching color I was learning how color worked.

Once I understood the physical laws of color—laws identified by science and purified by art—I began to use color intellectually—scientifically. I knew the reason for my choices.

DESIGNERS AND MANUFACTURERS

As a novice fabric buyer, manufacturer reps could not hide their amazement that this was my first buying experience. Had it happened once, I'd have discounted it, but I was told over and over, "You select fabrics like a veteran of many years." My research was paying off.

color is language, mood, and emotion, your emotion

It was in buying professionally that I first realized the waste that resulted from not understanding how color and line related to people. I put my fabric store together by my color collections. Customers would enter, survey the store and walk like homing pigeons to their correct place. They didn't officially know their colors, but they instinctively responded to them and bought them. Fabrics flew off the rack. On the opposite side, designers designed many fabrics that mixed colors in ways that would turn customers off rather than on. They created patterns that would not work well on the human body. Called dogs, these fabrics don't sell and they eat profits.

Later in my business career, I purchased clothing for a small boutique—part of my mall store. I walked and bought in the New York and Los Angeles garment district as well as the Dallas Mart. Over and over I saw waste from clothing designs that mixed colors and patterns in ways that confused customers. Or following what sold, I saw many clothing lines designed in 'safe' colors namely red, white, black, and beige.

On one of our New York buying trips, Robert and I sat in front of the men's section of Calvin Klein clothes in Saks Fifth Avenue. That season they featured warm colors of versions of yellow, green and teal blue. We watched several men come to the section, look over the clothes, reach, then hesitate, reach again, then hesitate as if wanting to buy, but not buying. Each time, I knew the gentlemen's preferred colors. I've often thought how easy it would be to get people to buy if manufacturers made clothes in colors customers wanted to touch, to hold, and to own.

Years of selling colored items has taught me the approximate percentages of people in each color collection. So rather than having to make large amounts of clothing in the current fashion color, you could make collections in a range of colors that met the needs of a broader range of people.

People instinctively reach out to their best colors. I've seen this instinctive "hold" in the closets of clients who refuse to throw away old, outdated clothing in their "right" colors. They usually apologize saying, "I don't know why I keep these old things." But, I know. The colors and styles of the "old" things line up perfectly with their coloring and body structure. Emotionally, throwing those items away would be like throwing away a bit of themselves. I understand.

Color is language. Color is mood. Color is emotion—your emotion. And color is science, just as music is science. You can cultivate your eye and color sense just as you cultivate your ear to music because laws govern color coordinations just as music laws govern harmony. The Beauty Code™ gives you the science to think about color intellectually as well as emotionally . . . to be able to give reasons for your choices and combinations of color. Most importantly The Beauty Code™ teaches you how to recognize and understand your instinctive feelings about color. You, like me, feel the effects of the colors you wear. Our color profile at www.mybeautycode.com shows and explains exactly how color applies to you.

The Beauty Code™ unlocks the secrets of Leonardo Da Vinci, Sir Isaac Newton and other great thinkers to guarantee your beauty. You will learn and understand how color works to create a beautiful, dynamic appearance. Rather than relying on the opinions of others, you will have the information, the code, to control and create your own accurate appearance signature. The Beauty Code™ is about identity—your identity.

We have your appearance down to a science. We know your Code—because we know the science.

IT MATTERS

Having a system of color and style based on science that we can trust to give us predictable results matters. It matters personally, professionally, and for designers and manufacturers. It matters for our confidence, our creativity, our fulfillment. It matters because it saves us time, energy, and money in preventing waste.

It matters to have a system that allows us to expand and hone our ability to create. It matters to expand our fulfillments. It matters to work from a platform of science that gives us predictability. Just like musicians create myriads of music from their system of notes and scales just like we know how much we weigh because we have a system of weights and measures, we need an accurate color system from which to work. Color deserves that much importance. So does style. It matters.

Each human being is beautiful and different from any other. This difference ought to be a celebration—a shout to the world of our own rarity, our own possibility.

The Beauty Code™ puts that power of celebration in your hands.

"The Beauty Code is to women what oxygen is to human beings – life. Every woman should radiate at the highest level they are capable of. With The Beauty Code, it is guaranteed! Thank you, Marilyn for helping us be the best that we can be as we share our love and light with the world."

–Vivian Phillips
Ms. Black Arizona 1987

FOOTNOTE

Along my path, I studied the work of Albert H. Munsell and his color wheel. Brilliant, Munsell invented the Munsell Color System. An American painter and art teacher, Munsell was born in Boston, Massachusetts, January 6, 1858.

While attending the Boston Normal Art School in the late 19th century, Albert Munsell was keenly aware that a practical theory of color did not exist. From his own work and experiments, he developed the Munsell Color System, a system that made it possible to discuss color scientifically.

Methodically, Munsell defined color in terms of hue, value, and chroma. Hue defines the actual color—red, blue, green, and others. Value defines the degree to which a color is light or dark. Chroma defines how strong or weak a color is, i.e. pastel or intense.

His system was the first widely-accepted color order system. It made the description of color accurate and convenient as well as an aid in teaching color. His color order system served as the foundation for other color order systems including CIELAB. Munsell's diaries tell of his visit to Gobelins to see Chevreul's scale of yarns. Diary 1 page 15 shows Munsell's notations of complementary colors.

Munsell published A Color Notation in 1905 and the Atlas of the Munsell Color System in 1915 defining the Munsell Color Standard which, before his work, had been an impossible task. His work was embraced by the scientific community. In 1914, he was invited to present his findings to the scientific communities of England, France, and Germany. His theory is still taught today.

His initial efforts were to find colors that were an equal distance apart. The nature of color vibrations made that impossible. His method was to spin discs containing different combinations of color.

From his experiments, Munsell felt yellow and red usurped too great a proportion of the color wheel. He asserted, "A total test of the circle gives great excess of orange, showing that red and yellow usurp too great a portion of the circumference." Consequently, he arbitrarily eliminated orange (a secondary combination of yellow and red) from the color spectrum, then created a new primary color wheel of only five colors: the three primary colors (red, yellow, and blue) and only two of the three secondary colors (green and purple). Arranged by value light to dark, the traditional color wheel places yellow, the lightest color at the top and purple, the darkest color, at the bottom, but Munsell placed green at the top of his color wheel with blue and purple on one side as cool colors and red and yellow on the other side as warm colors.

Munsell's concept contributes much to our understanding of the full dimensions of color. But for me, his system is diminished by his arbitrary decision to create a new primary color wheel eliminating orange. I puzzled over Munsell's experiments. We don't wear spinning colors. We base our perceptions of color on pigment combinations in the colors themselves. I did not understand his fiat against orange. Orange did not cease to exist in its correct place just because he arbitrarily decided red and yellow took too great a role on the color wheel. How could he eliminate a known scientific color from the whole-spectrum light color wheel and still have a scientifically valid system? This brought imbalance to the color wheel. It seemed presumptuous. I chose Newton's research and his color wheel of light as a scientific constant—never changing.

Munsell constructed his system around a circle with ten segments, arranging its colors at equal distances, and selecting them in such a way that opposing pairs would result in a chromatic mixture to balance colors in order to achieve color harmony and show how to find complementary colors.

After setting up his value-scale, Munsell selected samples from red (R), yellow (Y), green (G), blue (B), and purple (P) which to him—and his painter's eye—appeared equidistant not only from each other, but also from a grey of the same value. These became the basic hues of his system, and he provided an additional five mixtures—yellow-red (YR), green-yellow (GY), blue-green (BG), purple-blue (PB), and red-purple (RP)—arranging them in a circle around the previously mentioned neutral grey (N). The parameter Chroma 5 was arbitrarily assigned to all these ten main colors and their mixtures. The chroma scale is an open-ended scale and can reach values of up to 12 and 14 depending on the intensity of the colors used. Vermilion, for example, reaches this extreme position and is correspondingly abbreviated to 5R 5/14 in the Munsell notation, while pink, which is less saturated, is defined as 5R 5/4.

The outer gradients of the color-circle show how a total of 40 hues are created by dividing the original five color-hue intervals between the main hues, first into 10 then 20 and finally into 40 segments, once again in such a way that they will be perceived as equidistant. Their individualistic sounding names are also included.

A new Colour Atlas appeared in 1929, after Munsell's death, June 28, 1918 at age 60, this time under the title The Munsell Book of Colour. We still use this edition today.

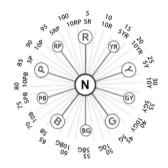

Munsell's color circle, created 1898

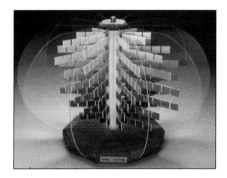

Munsell's three-dimensional model shows how fully Munsell defined the aspects of color (created 1915)

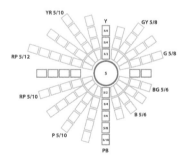

Munsell's three-dimensional model view looking from the top

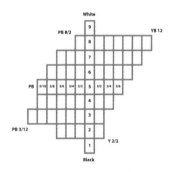

Munsell's three-dimensional model side view

Color is Science That

Always Affects You

Part I

knowing how to create beauty
without a beauty system **based on science**
is as difficult as
knowing how much you weigh
without a system of weights and measures.

Our Beauty Dilemma

"Charge all things you fashion with a breath of your own spirit."

Kahlil Gibran, *The Prophet*

chapter 1

Beauty is a guessing game.

Whether choosing makeup, wardrobe or home decor, the best we do on our own is trial and error. We complain that we have "nothing to wear" as we shuffle through a closet full of clothes. Why is that?

Knowing how to look good is a guessing game.

Ever since Eve told Adam that apples are "to-die-for," wanting to look good has constantly been on our mind and before our eyes. We [women and men] want to look attractive. But in trying to accomplish the appealing, pleasing look for ourselves that we see in the fashions, styles, and makeup constantly paraded before us in magazines and on television, we end up in a dilemma of confusion and frustration.

The attractiveness we want evades us. We have it one day. We lose it the next. We like one piece of clothing. We discard hundreds of others. When our look is put together correctly, we know it and others notice. When personal appearance is out of control, we feel that we are not, nor can we ever be attractive. Yet looking good remains central to our acceptance and well-being.

In my experience as a beauty professional, the greatest frustration women feel as they seek for beauty solutions is knowing how to consistently control how they look. Too often they don't know how to create the look they want. Others give up before they even start. Why? Because fashion misleads. One month we're told a color or style is "in." The next month we're told that it's "out." How can it be possible to relate to or even understand a constantly moving ideal?

As an intelligent woman, you know that looking good always remains central to your emotional and personal well-being. Yet, these constantly changing models of beauty leave millions of us feeling confused at best and inadequate at worst.

Today's beauty standard is out of date tomorrow. We try to understand. If we are fortunate enough to have something that works for us today, what do we do when fashions change tomorrow?

Wanting to know how, but lacking any substantive system for knowing the colors and styles that make us look good, we are left to play the guessing game. One that is difficult, if not impossible, to win. The "what to do" and "why you do it" of personal beauty remains an unknown—an unknown barrier to our own beauty. In order to break through this wall, we must first know the causes of our dilemma.

As you can see our problem begins with the images of beauty that are constantly fed to us. Most are simply unrealistic. We don't understand if and how these models will work for us. Nowhere do we have a system of scientific principles that we can depend on to help us.

It's amazing to realize that for decades, our culture's description of a good-looking woman has been a cover girl's face on an aerobic instructor's body. Fashion models are chosen because they are rail thin to make clothes hang on them as if on racks. A fashion model's size and proportion represent less than 5% of our population. How many women do you know that wear a size 5 to 7 dress, stand 5 feet 10 inches tall, and weigh less than 120 pounds? It is absurd for us to adopt that standard. The impact of this unreachable "ideal" constantly before us is not only impossible, it can be devastating as seen in the rising statistics of anorexia. If you are regularly pushed to an ideal you cannot achieve, you soon become frustrated or even neurotic.

Creating an attractive appearance without a system of beauty based on science is as difficult as knowing how much we weigh without a system of weights and measures.

When I began my career as an image consultant, I faced this guessing game. I studied hard, but textbooks and training failed to give me accurate rules or reliable answers to my questions and help my clients.

Why did some people look great in one color while others look washed-out? How could two women of similar build be so different in appearance; one looking slim and stunning while the other stubby and drab?

As I grew weary of this frustration myself, I began looking for answers. For over seven years, I researched in libraries across the United States to discover and then use correct laws of beauty and apply them to my clients.

Looking good always remains **central** to our *emotional* and *personal well-being*

My search started with style and health, then moved to color.

- I discovered a correlation between the science of color and the impact of color as we use it.

- I learned the science that enhances every proportion of our bodies when others look at us.

- I developed a system that provides any person, no matter their measurements and features, a proven predictable way to design makeup, choose clothing, and cut and color hair so they look and feel terrific.

- I learned how any woman can easily create timeless beauty.

In 1990, I launched Signairé®—A system of science for creating beautiful and dynamic appearances. It consisted of workbooks, color planners, cosmetics, and a skin care line. For years, I used and tested the Signairé system and cosmetics in my own salons. It worked with every client. Today I call my beauty system The Beauty Code™. My scientific color system is named The Science of Personal Color™.

Now this is what I know:

Far more than a fashion look, a hem length, or a hairstyle, beauty is a vibrant possibility for every woman.

In a sense, beauty is deeply mysterious, for one woman is essentially and distinctively different from another equally beautiful woman. We admire past beauties Sophia Loren, Princess Diana, Jacqueline Onassis and current beauties Julia Roberts, Angelina Jolie, and Cindy Crawford. No one could accuse them of cookie-cutter beauty. But we don't want to be repeats of them. We want to develop our own unique look—our own signature of appearance.

At the same time, beauty is not mysterious. It is as practical, hard-headed and hard-working as a balance sheet. It is not difficult. You can easily achieve it. I have learned and will share with you three keys that govern beauty. As well, I detail the science of color that relates to your personal beauty in the pages of this book and on my website, *www.mybeautycode.com.*

True and timeless beauty is the quintessential expression of your individuality. Beauty is a vibrant possibility for every woman. Yes, even for you. It is a harmonious meshing of your culture and customs with your own personality, character and moods. A smooth blending of your intrinsic qualities is possible by correctly combining these qualities with your cultural conventions of beauty to create a uniquely individual look, a signature of beauty created by understanding your unique beauty code.

It is the same for all women, anywhere in the world. As personal as your written signature, your beauty signature marks you as a woman in control of your own appearance and life.

*Beauty doesn't have to be **hard**, do what you already **do**, just differently*

True beauty is responsive to fashion but not slavish; contemporary, but timeless; distinctive, yet never faddish or overdone; daring, but not ridiculous; witty and fun, but not cute. It is the sum total of how you think, feel, look and act.

What you need to control the message of your appearance is the information, the knowledge, the system. You need your personal beauty code.

You can't wish your way to an attractive appearance. But you can apply the scientific principles in The Beauty Code™ and create your own beautiful signature appearance in harmony and integrity with who you are or are becoming.

Copying someone else's beauty code will not give you the results you want. Timeless beauty, signature beauty, starts with self-understanding. When you know, not just believe, that a color, style, or an accessory is right for you, you can use fashion to your advantage, rather than being disadvantaged by it. You can and will create your own unique statement in every fashion circle. You will know how. You will know why.

The path to your own signature appearance, to becoming your own best authority on yourself, begins with understanding three keys, the three main elements of The Beauty Code™—Color, Style, and Health.

COLOR

Color captures the dynamic power and the pulse of your personality every day when you dress. In The Beauty Code, you are introduced to my revolutionary new color system based on time-honored science. An exciting discovery, The Science of Personal Color™ System shows you how your hair, skin, and eye color naturally interact with makeup and clothing so you look outstanding all the time.

Professional and original, The Beauty Code alone offers The Science of Personal Color System that accurately connects all people, world-wide, with basic principles and qualities of color law including temperature, hue, value, intensity, complementary, and analogous effects. In doing so, the system exposes the inconsistencies, inaccuracies, and confusion inherent in any other color system. For a detailed personal color profile, go to Chapter 6 and www. mybeautycode.com. Your radiant beauty is assured–science ensures it!

STYLE

Style, for your personal use, consists of the lines and shapes you choose in clothing, accessories, and the patterns you use for applying your makeup and hairstyling. With discoveries in science as powerful as color itself, the complete Beauty Code Style System reveals how to handle the complex differences of the human body with new technology to give you meaningful style direction. The Beauty Code teaches you to be the expert in choosing your most attractive necklines, tops, jackets, pants, sleeves, hairstyles, and accessories, including jewelry and more.

Clothes, makeup, and hair all have personality messages that affect your style as well. Personality adds variety–spice–to your appearance. We each have several unique personality aspects that we like to express in different ways–different clothing styles in different color combinations and cosmetic applications. When you take The Beauty Code Audit online, you will discover those personality expressions that best speak the message you want spoken.

HEALTH

Radiant vitality and health is always a part of remembered beauty. If you have troubled skin, damaged hair, or poor general health, you know that your appearance suffers. So you can enjoy good health, I put together my Diet of Light and Life. I stay healthy by using this plan which I share with you on my website, *www.mybeautycode.com.*

Ultimately, The Beauty Code is about identity. Your identity. The Beauty Code helps you accurately define that identity. It helps you understand better who you are and how to confidently express your distinctiveness in your personal expressions of yourself.

A bold new system of total appearance based on the science of light, The Beauty Code's unique difference from all other appearance systems is in its application of science.

*Rather than being **chained** to the **closet**, a **hairstyle**, and the **mirror, the woman** who has formulated her **own beauty signature** can make appearance decisions **swiftly** and **accurately***

You want more than pretty.

You want confident.

You want capable.

Your clothing, hairstyle, makeup, home, car, and more are simply tools to build upon your existing platform of personal identity. Through the intelligent use of color, wardrobe, and makeup you can enhance your appearance while making a personal statement of who you are.

So since there is only one you, focus on your individuality. Represent the best of yourself—this is wisdom. With the science of The Beauty Code, you get predictability in looking good. You will look and feel beautiful. People will compliment you.

Instead of concentrating on what's less than perfect, I encourage you to see a larger vision. Bring the beauty you have inside outside. Reveal the total woman that you are, the positive qualities that make you special, unique, and remembered.

Beauty
is always
governed
by the
intelligent
use of
knowledge

Beauty, like any other form of power, is governed by the intelligent use of knowledge. As you read and use this information step-by-step, you will govern your personal appearance. The message of appearance declares in undeniable terms who you are, and even how you feel about yourself. Create this message to enhance your personal influence—an enhancement that leaves fashion subservient to personal and timeless beauty.

Ultimately, The Beauty Code is more than color, style, or appearance. It's about light—about discovering the light in yourself and the effect of your light on those you influence. Color comes from light. As a person of color, you are a person of light.

I love The Beauty Code. I love the "knowing" of how beauty works. I love not worrying about how I look. I love seeing beauty come alive in my clients as they unlock and use their own Beauty Codes. I love sharing their self-discovery. I would never want to go back to the frustration of "unknowing" that I lived with before I founded The Beauty Code.

If I could stand all my clients in front of you, you'd see women of every shape and size. Some rail thin, some overweight, but each radiant and remarkably distinct in a pleasing way. Each is presenting her own unique beauty, accurate to her. The results in the lives of my clients have been more rewarding, more fulfilling than I ever expected. To this I give credit to the Master Source of Light and Creator of all.

Thousands of women and men have successfully used the color system found in The Beauty Code to create their own unique signature in appearance. Consistently they report that the new confidence they get when using the system makes them more relaxed about their appearance and decor decisions. They save time, money, and frustration. They enjoy their purchases more. Best of all, they feel a renewed energy that spills over into other areas of their lives. No longer intimidated by media beauties, these women are beautiful women in their own right and world. Men also enjoy having straightforward guidelines that knowing their code gives them to handle their appearance and the impact of appearance in their lives.

Just like every woman, you have a hope, a dream, a contribution unique to you. You have a beautiful signature of yourself within—as unique, personal, and valuable as your own written signature. You deserve accurate, practical knowledge to help you bring that signature statement to the surface. The Beauty Code gives you this knowledge. It is an individual effort with individual results, but armed with the right knowledge, any woman can achieve it. Any woman or man can learn how to replace frustration and confusion with authentic beauty—with an appearance signature—that reveals the inner person through the outer appearance, harmonizing the two, making wholeness and authenticity out of previous contradiction and haphazardness.

Imagine having a sure way to sift through the constant flow of media and fashion, knowing how it does or does not apply to you. Imagine always looking terrific. Imagine being your own best fashion and appearance expert. Imagine the confidence, the security you will have from that fabulous feeling of knowing.

One of my overweight clients came into my salon every six weeks. Half of our clientele was from a college nearby. Every time she came in, one or more students would comment on how attractive she was. Regardless of male or female, no one ever commented on her weight. I'd expect to hear comments about her weight but they never came. Not once. What I did hear was how attractive she was, over and over again. A great lesson on the value of looking good.

Another overweight client followed her Beauty Code color and style directions perfectly. She had a design background so she designed and sewed her own clothes. She received so many compliments on how good she looked that

Since there is only **one** *of* **you,** **focus** *on your* **individuality**

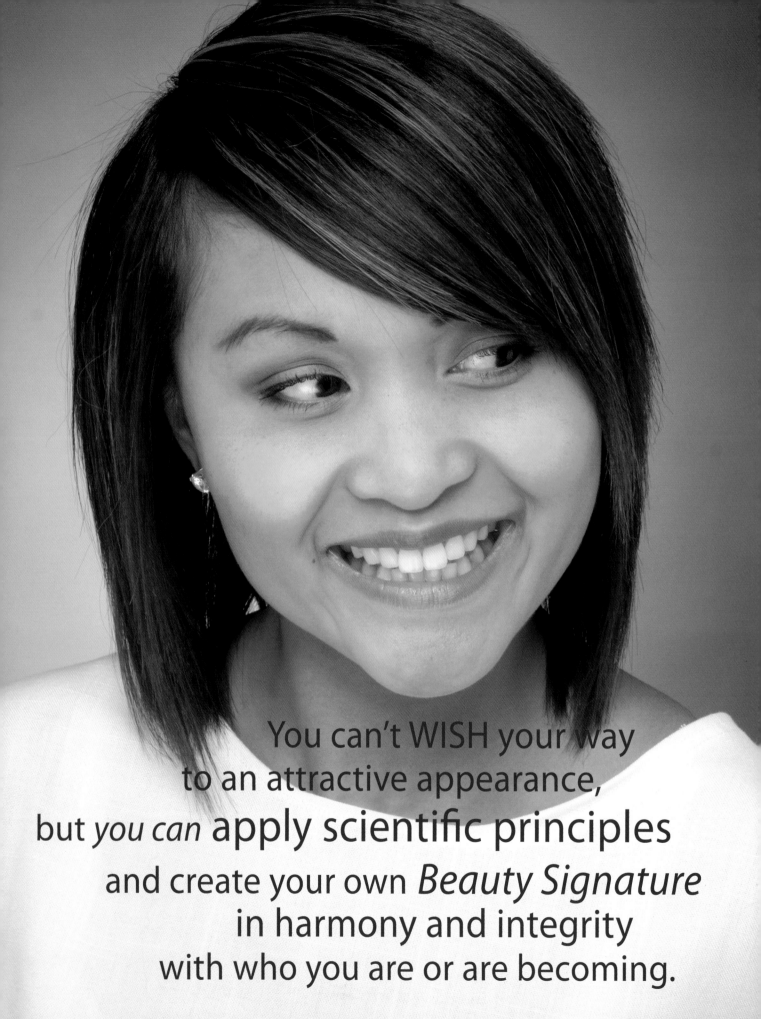

You can't WISH your way
to an attractive appearance,
but *you can* apply scientific principles
and create your own *Beauty Signature*
in harmony and integrity
with who you are or are becoming.

it reinforced her confidence to stay with a diet program. She looked even more amazing with her new slim figure.

Lauri says of her experience with her Beauty Code, "I found that by putting on my makeup and clothes in the right colors, I felt good and was better able to face the challenges that came up. Once I'd slept in the car for an overnight cold weather outing. A work associate said, 'Lauri, you look so put together today. You look nice.' It took me off-guard but I knew it was because I was in the right colors. I put my makeup on first thing every day.

I get unexpected compliments everyday from strangers, family and friends. It still surprises me. It's so easy to look good with the Beauty Code. I just pull from my closet and it works. I don't stress about how I look anymore."

One of the least-understood aspects of beauty is that it is highly liberating. Rather than being chained to the closet, the hairstyle, and the mirror, a woman who has formulated her own beauty signature can make appearance decisions swiftly and accurately. She has created a look that expresses herself and thus leaves her free for the important matters of her life. It's no coincidence that women with truly timeless beauty do not make a career out of being beautiful. Rather, they make significant contributions to society—contributions that make them highly-respected within professional circles as well as widely-admired for their attractive and distinctive appearance.

This is the mooring of real beauty.

You and I make important color decisions every day, often many times a day. We need a competent tool—a reliable system—to help us. Understanding the science of color allows us to use color as a tool—a tool for discovering and revealing ourselves. With *The Beauty Code™*, you never again need be dependent on the opinions of others. Rather, you will direct and fashion others' opinion with your own sense of style,

your own code of beauty.

The Color Code
of Always
Looking Good

Wherever there is light, color follows . . . an inescapable, intriguing, and motivating fact of the physical world.

Physics has explained this phenomenon.

Art has explored its influence.

Design has coordinated its application.

And psychology has made significant strides in defining the power of light and color in treating depression and other emotional and neurological conditions that we face.

Recognizing this, institutions now find that choosing the right colors for their office is a requirement for success. Hospitals choose soothing, relaxing colors to calm patients. Restaurants choose stimulating, exciting colors to enliven their clients . . . and their appetites.

We all know we prefer some colors to other colors. But, why? Why do we look healthier, happier, and more at ease in the world in some colors than in others? Indeed, why do we feel better? Why do we make a better impression, experience increased well-being, and have greater comfort in our environments?

In the past, we have been slow to recognize that the use of color provides us not only with beauty and variety, but also with an increase or decrease in effectiveness and emotional well-being. And even when we have recognized this fact, we have not had a process, method, or system by which the physics of color could be made understandable and useful for us to use in our daily lives.

Several schools of color analysis flourished in recent decades. Some people found them successful, but most did not. Among reputable professionals, color analysis was a fad, only one step away from professional quackery. Like millions of others, I studied most of them, tried several willing to believe—and ended up disappointed. We were told we were a season of the year as though colors were a function of the calendar, but we were never told why we "worked" in only part of the year—Winter, Summer, Autumn, or Spring. The oversimplified Color Key System tried to fit all races into two keys, warm and cool. Other systems tried to reform or expand these two systems, telling us we get our coloring from a month of the year, or a time of the day—morning, noon, or night.

We were told a color looks good on us but we were never told why. We were given swatches and told to buy only items that match these samples. But nowhere were we educated about the physical principles upon which color is based. So when new fashionable colors came along—teal, magenta, or apricot—still, we were helpless to know whether it would work for us because we lacked the scientific foundation for understanding the relationships and revelations of which color is capable. Confused and frustrated, many have abandoned the idea that a useful system of color really exists. But you and I make important color decisions every day, often many times a day. We need a competent tool—a reliable system—to help us.

The Beauty Code™ introduces you to The Science of Personal Color™ System, a useful system of color that I developed after long study of Masters in science and art. It is useful because it is scientific. It has proven to work on thousands of women and men of all races. It keeps the unfulfilled promises pledged by other systems.

Figure 1

Sir Isaac Newton

The earliest modern scientific analyses of light and color were those of Sir Isaac Newton,[1] the famed seventeenth-century British scientist, who "transformed the science of optics."[2]

Newton "discovered the theory of the light spectrum by passing a fine beam of sunlight through a glass prism, thus dividing it by refraction into its component colours. By passing the coloured light back through the prism, he also showed that although the colours could be reunited into homogeneous white light, no single colour could

Pure light contains all color.

Black is the absence of any light; no color is seen.

Red, yellow, and blue are the primary colors; they were originally named "primary colors" by Newton during his experiments because they were the most basic colors found in nature. They could not be created or made from combining any other color or colors. Yet from these three colors, plus black and white, every other possible color could be mixed.

Little by little, understanding the physics of color allows you to use color as a tool—a tool for discovering and revealing yourself. Physics gives you the key to the relationships and revelations of which color is capable. Once you understand the science and aesthetics of color, you need never again be at the mercy of color ignorance. You will never again be dependent on the opinions of others. Rather, you will direct and fashion others' opinion with your own sense of style, your own signature. Looking your best reinforces you because when you look your best, you do your best and work to be your best.

In my search to connect the science of color to you and me, I studied about the Impressionists. The Impressionists taught us that color is the first factor of beauty, which proves to be of great significance. Cosmetics, clothes, and home décor are color—just in different forms. Color is the number one factor of a pleasing appearance because it is most easily seen, the most emotionally registered. We speak of loving or hating a color. We feel color. That is, we feel the effects of color.

be changed. By this means he demonstrated that light is a compound of all the spectral colours."[3] Newton observed that light breaks into three identifiable colors—red, yellow, and blue—with an infinite variety of shades between.

This passage through a prism is called refraction. The light is deflected from a straight path as it passes from one medium (air) into another (the glass prism) in which its velocity is different. The refracted light makes the color spectrum appear in tiny rainbows on whatever flat surface they (the refracted light) fall on. Bending that line of colors into a circle creates the color wheel.

Color is science, just as music is science

Think about it. You use color in all your choices in personal beauty, for clothing, cosmetics, hair color, furnishings, housewares, decorating fabrics, wallpapers, drapes, landscaping, even motor vehicles. Just the effects of the right colors can make you look and feel better, happier—more fulfilled.

The right colors multiply your physical virtues. They make your features more distinct and give your skin a natural, healthy radiance.

Color is science, just as music is a science. You can cultivate your eye and sense of color just as you cultivate your ear to music because laws govern color harmony just as laws govern music harmony. The coordination and relationships of color are as scientific as the music laws that govern harmony. This means you can understand color intellectually as well as emotionally—and be able to give reasons for your choices and combinations of color. It can be learned.[4]

The color story which follows, explains the science of color in simple terms. It tells you how color can scientifically create or destroy your beauty and presence.

THE STORY OF COLOR AND YOU

All colors come from light. In the dark there are no colors. On a foggy day, all colors become muted. Because pure white light contains every color, when we look at a rainbow or light through a prism, we see light broken into wavelengths of color.

Primary, or first source colors, are yellow, red, and blue . . .

Figure 2

. . . with secondary color mixtures of orange, purple, and green.

Figure 3

This is called the color spectrum.

We use color in all our choices... clothing, cosmetics... ... even motor vehicles.

When we connect the primary and secondary colors into a circle, we get . . .

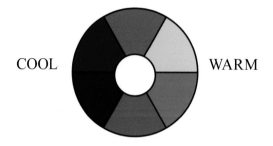

COOL   WARM

The Color Wheel

Figure 4

Third source or Tertiary Colors come from mixing a primary and a secondary color together. The primary color name is said first.

Figure 5

| BLUE GREEN | RED ORANGE | YELLOW GREEN |
| BLUE PURPLE | RED PURPLE | YELLOW ORANGE |

When we add black to colors, they get darker or shaded.

When we add white—they get lighter.

HOW LIGHT MAKES COLOR
Light mixes with pigments to make different colors.

An apple is red because the pigment in the apple absorbs all the colors in light except red. The color red is reflected back into our eyes and we see a red apple, as illustrated in the example below.

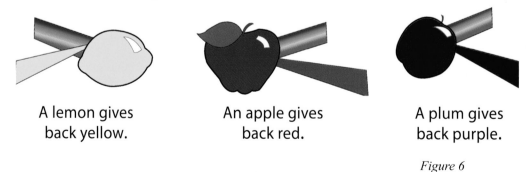

A lemon gives
back yellow.

An apple gives
back red.

A plum gives
back purple.

Figure 6

People are different colors because everyone has different amounts of color pigments. Some have more red. Some have more yellow. Some have more blue. We are all born with unbalanced proportions of the primary colors; one primary color is strongest, one is moderately weak and one is weakest. This subject will be discussed in more detail in the next chapter.

My best colors may not be your best colors because you and I have different mixtures of the primary colors in our skin. This makes us individual and our individuality makes the world interesting. If we all had the same mixtures of primary colors in our skin, then we would all look the same and our world would be boring.

HOW COLOR LAW DEVELOPS A DYNAMIC APPEARANCE

CONTRASTING COLORS *(Complementary Colors)* Colors that are opposite on the color wheel. Complementary colors make each other look stronger, like red ornaments on a green Christmas tree.	**SIMILAR COLORS** *(Analogous Colors)* Colors that are neighbors on the color wheel. Analogous colors make each other look weaker, like blue ornaments on a green tree.

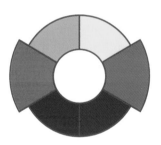

Figure 7

The red makes the green look stronger and greener. The green makes the red look redder.

The blue and green weaken each other because they both share the color blue.

COLORS AND CHRISTMAS TREES

The Color Wheel in the center emphasizes how red and green are opposites of each other. The red makes the green appear stronger and greener. The green makes the red appear redder. The blue and green weaken each other because they both share the color blue.

CONTRASTING COLORS

 If you have more RED in your skin and wear GREEN, you will look redder or flushed because the GREEN strengthens the RED.

 If you have more YELLOW in your skin and wear PURPLE, you will look YELLOW or jaundiced because the purple strengthens the YELLOW.

 If you have more BLUE in your skin and you wear ORANGE, you look bluer or washed out because ORANGE strengthens BLUE.

SIMILAR COLORS

 If you have more RED in your skin, wearing RED softens the RED in your skin and strengthens GREEN, a mix of your weak BLUE and YELLOW.

 If you have more YELLOW in your skin, wearing YELLOW softens the YELLOW in your skin and strengthens PURPLE, a mix of your weak BLUE and RED.

 If you have more BLUE in your skin, wearing BLUE softens the BLUE in your skin and strengthens ORANGE, a mix of your weak RED and YELLOW.

Figure 8

So how does color law affect your appearance?

Similar (or analogous) colors as seen above have a special effect that helps you look terrific. While they soften your strongest color, they are also busy, at the same time, making your weakest colors stronger.

We do not get our coloring from the seasons, a time of day, or month of the year. We get our coloring from light interacting with the different pigments found in our bodies. When you understand how color works and you know your personal coloring, you'll wear colors that are similar or analogous to your own coloring. Doing this will bring your own three primary colors into balance, the balance of light; your best colors will weaken your strongest primary color and strengthen your two weaker primary colors. This will make you look healthy and vibrant because you are using color to work for you instead of against you.

You become your own prism when you dress in your correct colors. You radiate the power, clarity, and energy of white light. You have greater presence. You look and feel empowered. You can then, like thousands of other Beauty Code users, move confidently and successfully into other areas of your life.

IT'S A PRINCIPLE OF LIGHT

In a physics lab, if you were to place three prisms, one in each primary color–red, yellow, and blue–over each other and shine a light from top to bottom, you would see at the bottom a spot of pure light because these three colors complete the vibrations needed to make light. This is the principle by which the colors in The Beauty Code™ make you look so radiant–so good.

Figure 9

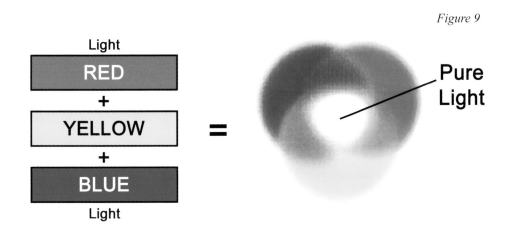

PURE LIGHT CONTAINS EVERY COLOR

Pure light is made up from combining red, yellow, and blue and combinations of those colors through a prism.

*We do **not** get our **coloring** from the **seasons,** a time of day, or month of the year.*

*We get our **coloring** from **light** interacting with the different **pigments** found in **our bodies.***

"Whenever I wear clothes in my colors with my right makeup, I hear lots of compliments. People will say, 'You look pretty.' When I wear something out of my color range, people may compliment the shirt or jacket—but never me.'
—Alexia

Audrey, a college student, says it this way, "Having this understanding of color gave me a better picture of myself and my personality . . . what kind of person I really am. It explains why I am drawn to some things and not others. It has helped me express myself in a whole new way. Because I portray myself better, I get better, more positive feedback. Without the colors in The Beauty Code, I would choose traditional, safe color combinations. But now I'm putting colors together in entirely new ways that are different and exciting. I have a much better sense of myself."

Cosmetologist, Pamela G., feels this about her Beauty Code experience: "I love the Beauty Code. I feel like a whole new life is blooming for me. It is something I've been looking for. I want people to be enrolled for the self-esteem part of it -- for the confidence it gives you."

This book gives you complete, clear information that you can use to look wonderful today, next week and ten years from now. Every area of The Beauty Code Color System--The Science of Personal Color™--is based on scientific principles as constant as rainbows and prisms. This color system won't change with each new twist of fashion. Yet the principles work in every fashion change.

Only science can end the gimmick—the guessing game and dilemma of beauty. You have in your hands that code of color science.

CHAPTER 2 NOTES

[1] A More In-Depth Look at the Scientific Study of Light and Color

Newton's experiment with the prism is described on pages 30-31. In 1672, Newton presented his ideas on light and color to the Royal Society of London, the foremost scientific community of the day. In 1704 he published his findings in a treatise titled *Opticks*. I use the Dover Publications, New York, N.Y., 1979 edition, by I. Bernard Cohen. Newton's quotes are indicated by page number below.

Although the action of the prism on a beam of light was not new, no one had studied the exact mechanism involved. Newton felt that the character of the light was not actually changed by the prism, but that sunlight contained a mix of different colors and the prism, through the process of refraction, bent each differently. He said, "The light of the Sun consists of rays differently refrangible." Newton named the prismatic band of light created by the prism a "spectrum," a term still used today (pg 30-31).

When Michael Clapier, my research assistant, appeared with this quotation, I felt elated. I had been looking for immutable concepts—principles as calculable as geometry, as precise as algebra. Newton continued: "All the productions and appearances of Colours in the world are derived not from any change caused in Light . . . but only by the various mixtures or separations of rays, by virtue of their different refrangibility or reflexibility. . . . **In this respect the Science of Colours becomes a speculation as truly mathematical as any other part of opticks.**" (page 244)

I knew color was a property of light, but I was overwhelmed with this clear statement that color, as a property of light, could be computed mathematically. Finally I had confirmation of my intuition that color and color reactions are as precise as mathematics and that a system of color could be created based on color law.

A third statement by Newton helped me understand the operation of light: The colors of light in the spectrum "cannot appear coloured by any means [other] than by reflecting those which either are of their own colour, or which by mixture must produce it." (page 181)

The color of each person's skin is created by a combination of colors. Therefore, each person's skin is a different color with varying shades of hue, value, tone, and temperature. We each possess different combinations of the primary colors and melanin. **Skin color, in short, is an element of our appearance that remains individually our own.**

[2] Harvey Flaumenhaft, "Introduction," in Newton's Optical Writings: A Guided Study, by Dennis L. Sepper (New Brunswick, N.J.: Rutger's University Press, 1994), xii.

[3] Ibid., xi.

[4] Standard Color Terminology

Hue or tone:	The name of the color; for example, fuchsia, khaki, aqua, mauve.
Temperature:	The warmth (degree of yellow or orange) or coolness (degree of blue or green) of a color.
Value:	The light, medium, or dark gradations of color; for example, white-gray-black; beige-tan-brown; light pink through dark pink to red or burgundy.
Intensity:	The amount of pigment which creates the brightness, dullness or richness of a color; for example, an ordinary green, when it is bright and intense, is grass green or spring green. Khaki is of dull intensity, but sage or spruce is of rich intensity.

My color
differs from your color
because we each have a
unique combination
of red, yellow, blue, and brown—
an individual color signature.

Your Skin Begins Your Color Code

Why do different colors work better on different people?

Why is it that some clothing sits unused in your closet while other clothing continues to get used, long after it should have been tossed?

Your skin has a unique combination of the primary colors – red, yellow, and blue. The amount of red, yellow, and blue in your skin is controlled by the pigmentation of your skin, hair, and eyes. This pigmentation in your skin, hair, and eyes makes up your coloring. Your personal coloring determines the colors you will be attracted to and the ones you won't like. This is why some clothing sits unused in your closet. Just compare the colors of the clothes you wear all the time with the colors of the clothes that just gather dust. You'll see the same colors repeated in the clothing you wear often.

Rework colors of your clothing to interact with the color scheme of your body. While some colors make you look great, others make you look pale, washed out or just "off." Whether we understand it or not, these color interactions are always present. Called Color Law or optics, laws in the science of physics determine these interactions. Color Law governs the relationships between different colors. Some color relationships create balance; some create dissonance. When you understand how Color Law works, you will have a very powerful tool to select only those clothes that work best for the unique color scheme of your body. With The Science of Personal Color™ System found in The Beauty Code™, you will significantly expand your color options of empowering colors. After you read every word of this chapter, you will know more about personal coloring than the most famous designers and makeup artists. So let's move ahead in your understanding.

Your skin has three layers: the epidermis, the dermis, and the subcutaneous (fatty) tissue.

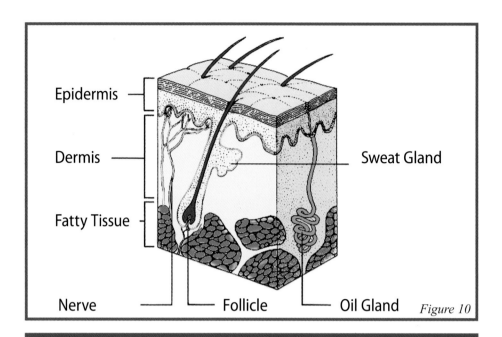

Figure 10

YOUR SKIN

The three layers of your skin are illustrated here:
Epidermis, Dermis, and Subcutaneous (fatty) Tissue

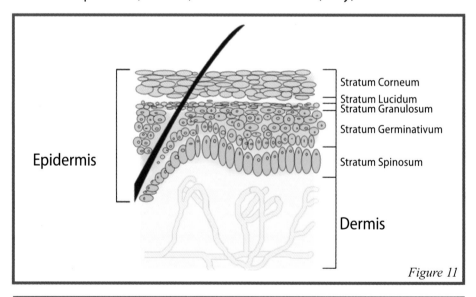

Figure 11

THE EPIDERMIS

Diagram of the epidermis layer of the skin

THE EPIDERMIS

The epidermis, a paper-thin layer that forms the outer protective layer of your skin, has five layers of cells from the outermost to the innermost:

1. The Stratum Corneum, also known as the "horny layer," consists of between fifteen and forty rows of dying cells filled with a tough, waterproof protein called keratin[1] that keeps fluids from passing through the skin. This layer makes the skin tough and sheds off in thin flakes. The number of rows of keratin cells differs in people which explains the difference in individuals' skin density.

2. The Stratum Lucidum, a transitional clear layer composed of cells through which light can pass.

3. The Stratum Granulosum, a granular layer made up of one or two rows of dying cells containing small grains of a substance called keratohyalin that becomes keratin when the cells reach the horny layer.

4. The Stratum Spinosum, a spinous layer composed of between four and ten rows of living cells with spine-like projections where the cells touch each other.

5. The Stratum Germinativum, or basal layer, which consists of a single row of tall, narrow, living cells. This layer also includes cells called melanocytes that produce a brown pigment called melanin.[2] The skin replaces itself completely in forty-five to seventy-five days, or about every two months.

THE DERMIS

The dermis, the source of red in our coloring, is chiefly composed of blood vessels, nerve endings, and connective tissue. The dermis attaches to the epidermis by tiny bumps, called papilla, that fit into tiny pits on the underside of the epidermis which houses the papilla, making our skin sensitive to touch.

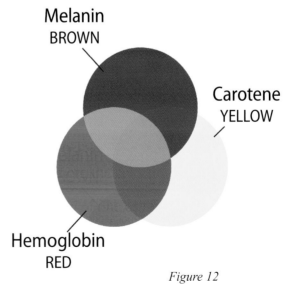

Melanin
BROWN

Carotene
YELLOW

Hemoglobin
RED

Figure 12

THE SUBCUTANEOUS TISSUE

The subcutaneous tissue, a much thicker layer beneath the dermis, consists mainly of connective tissue, blood vessels, and fat cells.

THE COLOR OF OUR SKIN

Each of the primary colors is present in our bodies. Deborah Chase, in her book *The Medically Based No-Nonsense Beauty Book*, explains, "There are three important pigments that lend color to the skin: melanin, which gives skin its brown tones; carotene, which imparts the yellow skin tones; and hemoglobin, the red pigment in the blood, which gives skin its pink and red tones. These three pigments act together to produce the skin's ultimate color on the same principle that causes you to see green when you look at a blue light through a yellow filter. Our skin color is actually a blend of various pigmentations of differing colors. The three pigments—melanin, carotene, and hemoglobin—joining one another to produce our flesh tones.[3]

WHAT ABOUT BLUE?

In Chapter One we established that all color comes from three primary colors—red, yellow, and blue—with shading from black and white. Deborah Chase has explained where we get the red, yellow, and shading colors in our skin. But where do we get blue? To answer this we must understand the nature of blue. And to understand the nature of blue, we must refresh our knowledge of the nature of all color.

THE WAVELENGTHS OF COLOR

Modern physicist, Robert A. Schluter says, "Centuries ago, Sir Isaac Newton passed a beam of sunlight through a glass prism, and opened a whole new world of understanding of color. He determined that all colors are contained in white (i.e. day sunlight) and that each color region is bent differently by a transparent prism, blue bent most and red bent least, yielding the color spectrum seen in the familiar rainbow (illustrated on page 47).

"There are two other fundamental physical phenomena that determine the observation of color.

"The first is interference. A century after Newton, it was determined that light was really a traveling wave possessing a wavelength. Those waves could line up, resonate, and get stronger. Or on the other hand, they could negate each other, interfere destructively, resulting in low light intensity.

The vivid blue in kingfisher and peacock feathers … comes from light scattering due to the irregular construction of the feathers.

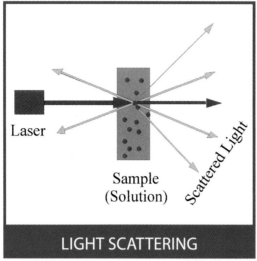

LIGHT SCATTERING

Figure 13

When light waves hit an irregular or rough surface, it bounces off at a ninety degree angle in many directions.

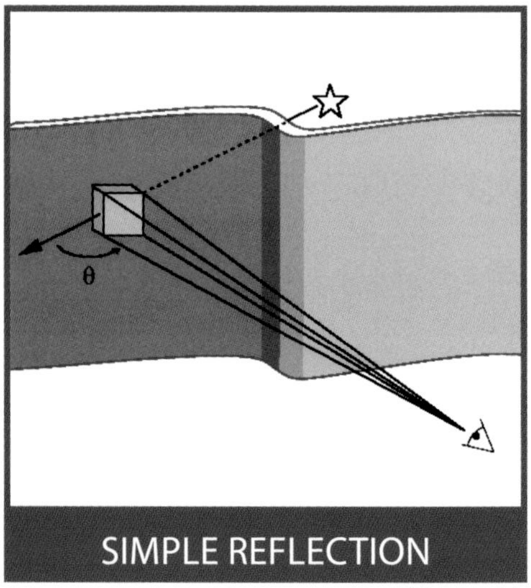

SIMPLE REFLECTION

Figure 14

When light hits a smooth surface, it bounces off in a straight line at a ninety degree angle to the angle of impact.

Newton's color law, correlated with the colors found in our bodies, gives us an effective color system for people worldwide

Different wavelengths, or colors, lined up differently, so the colors were separated. The effect is set up by reflecting light from an orderly lineup of microscopic elements, dots or cells. A most dramatic case of this is shown in the design and construction of the feathers of the peacock, the king fisher bird, or in brilliantly colored butterfly wings. [If these feathers or wings are hit or crushed, they are no longer brilliantly colored but become black, losing all color]. This appearance is called 'iridescence,' meaning colors which vary strongly with the angle of view. A thin film of oil on water will produce iridescent colors by interference.

"No structure is visible in the human body that produces iridescence, but, in addition to birds and butterflies, it is seen in some spectacular gemstones like the opal and in 'holographic' display jewelry."[4]

Blue is also produced through the occurrence of *light scattering*. Light scattering or Rayleigh Scattering is the phenomenon of light being absorbed and very quickly re-emitted in all directions. This happens when light waves hit the irregular surface of the earth. They quickly scatter in all directions.

Reflection happens when light hits a smooth surface like a shiny piece of steel and bounces off in a straight line at a ninety degree angle to the angle of impact. But if the ray hits an irregular or rough surface, it bounces off in many directions. Each

Figure 15

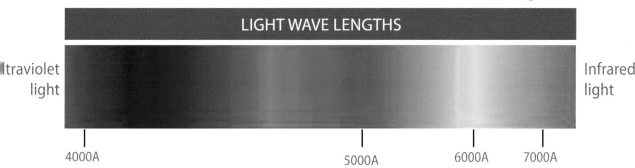

LIGHT WAVE LENGTHS

Ultraviolet light

Infrared light

4000A   5000A   6000A   7000A

The diagram above illustrates the difference in wave lengths among the colors of the rainbow. Red has the longest wavelength, while blue has the shortest.

*The **ricocheting movement** of **light** produces a **blue color***

part of the beam or ray strikes in a different place so each takes its ninety degree course in a different direction from the irregular bit of surface that it strikes.

In this way, light splits and ricochets. This ricocheting action of light produces the blue tone in the sky and the blue color in large bodies of water. Air in a room is colorless. Water in a glass is colorless. The ricocheting movement of light produces a blue color when seen in depth or distance.

The shorter the wavelength of the light, the more it scatters. Blue, the shortest and most energetic wavelength, scatters the most; red, the longest wavelength, scatters least. Blue, being at the upper end of the spectrum, has the shortest and most energetic wavelength, so it absorbs and re-radiates more power than other colors with longer waves. In other words, the sky is blue because "sunlight comes in from one direction and blue light is scattered out in all directions by the electrons in atoms of the atmosphere so that an observer looking toward the sky in any direction sees this blue light.[5]

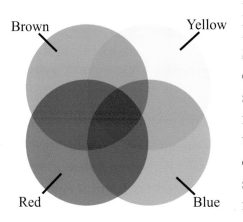

Brown   Yellow

Red   Blue

Figure 16

For the more technically minded among you, Dr. Robert A. Schluter explains Rayleigh Scattering this way, "The other well-known color effect comes when separate randomly-spaced elements, ideally molecules, are illuminated by white light. The simplest case is that of sunlight impinging on the air molecules of the atmosphere. The molecules are stimulated to re-radiate energy with a maximum at ninety degrees to the incident beam, that is, to the side, and preferentially in the blue part of the spectrum. The red part is largely undeviated. This is called Rayleigh Scattering after the British physicist John William Strutt, Lord Rayleigh, 1842-1919, who identified the phenomenon and thereby explained why the sunset is red due to direct rays from the sun, the sky is blue due to the flood of side-radiated light scattered and re-scattered by the molecules, the centers of scattering. When light passes through a mostly transparent complex medium containing other elements it undergoes a version of Rayleigh Scattering. It diffuses with the blue end of the spectrum tending to emerge in a different set of directions than the red-orange end."[6]

Gary Waldman, author of *Introduction to Light: The Physics of Light, Vision and Color*, notes, "The blue eyes of humans are blue not because the irises have a blue pigment, but rather because they have a number of small scattering particles in front, giving Rayleigh Scattering seen against the dark of the rear layers of the iris."[7]

THE BLUE IN OUR SKIN

Now, let's think of your skin. Skin can achieve its blue tones from light scattering in the top two layers of the skin, the lucidum and corneum, by much the same process through which eyes have a blue tint. The amounts of blue and yellow would be influenced by the thickness of the corneum layer (between 15 to 40 layers). A thicker corneum (40 layers) would be more yellow and allow less blue to come through; a thinner corneum (15 layers) would allow more blue to show through.

In our skin, as light passes through the lucidum and corneum strata and encounters the stratum granulosum, the irregular granular structure of this third layer causes the blue wave length of light to ricochet, thus causing bluish tones in the skin. The exact amount is governed by the density of the stratum corneum.[8]

Melanin takes on different hues according to the strength of the other dominant colors in our skin in the same way that we can have a red brown, a yellow brown, or a blue brown. People with a great deal of melanin are browner or darker. People with little melanin are less brown or lighter.

As you absorb this information, it becomes clear why your color differs from my color. It's because you and I each have different proportions of the primary colors and melanin caused by the differing construction of our skin.

Skin color combinations are as **varied** *as the* **degrees** *in the* **color spectrum**

This difference in construction gives each of us a unique color pattern, an individual pigment code composed of the primary colors and melanin present in our skin.

The colors we each wear interact with our skin, hair, and eye coloring. Some colors make us look wonderful; some make us look terrible. At *www.mybeautycode.com*, you can get a personal color profile that shows you the wonderful and terrible effects color can have on your personal coloring. Whether we understand it or not, color interaction is happening all the time and it affects how we look. The way colors affect and relate to each other is called Color Law.

This we learn about next.

"What makes makeup look natural? Wearing the right colors! My makeup never looked natural until I started using Beauty Code makeup in the right colors and wearing clothes in the right colors. The Beauty Code Color System gives us the science to know our right colors."
—Eileen B.

CHAPTER 3 NOTES

[1] Keratin. The number of rows of keratin cells differs in people, which explains the difference in individuals' skin density. Keratin—waterproof protein. Caroten—orange photosynthetic pigment.

[2] William Montagna, Alvert M. Kligman, Kay S. Carlisle, *Atlas of Normal Human Skin* (New York: Springer-Verlag, 1992), 24.

[3] Deborah Chase, *The Medically Based No-Nonsense Beauty Book* (New York: Alfred A. Knopf, Inc., 1974), 175.

[4] Robert A. Schluter, "Bending and Wavelengths of Light." Personal email and addition to book. (23 October 2007).

Northwestern University, College of Arts and Sciences, and Graduate School, Professor of Physics and Astronomy 1961-1992. Emeritus 1992- present.

Dr. Schluter published 120 research papers and portions of three books arising from experimental research in nuclear physics and elementary particle physics 1947–1988 carried out at University of Chicago, Massachusetts Institute of Technology, Fermi National Accelerator Laboratory, Argonne National Laboratory, Brookhaven National Laboratory, Princeton-Penn Accelerator, and University of California Lawrence Radiation Laboratory.

[5] Gary Waldman, *Introduction to Light: The Physics of Light, Vision, and Color* (Englewood Cliffs, N.J.: Prentice-Hall, 1983), 172-74.

[6] Robert A. Schluter, "Bending and Wavelengths of Light." Personal email and addition to book. (23 October 2007).

[7] Gary Waldman, *Introduction to Light: The Physics of Light, Vision, and Color* (Englewood Cliffs, N.J.: Prentice-Hall, 1983), 172-74.

[8] Skin Color.

Although I have yet to encounter any scientific studies of light penetration of living human skin, far better documented is the fact that the three pigments of red, yellow, and blue, plus the brown pigment, melanin, interact to produce the skin's perceived color. This effect is not difficult to understand. Our skin color is actually a blend of various pigmentation of differing colors.

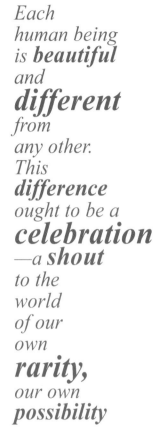

*Each
human being
is **beautiful**
and
different
from
any other.
This
difference
ought to be a
celebration
—a **shout**
to the
world
of our
own
rarity,
our own
possibility*

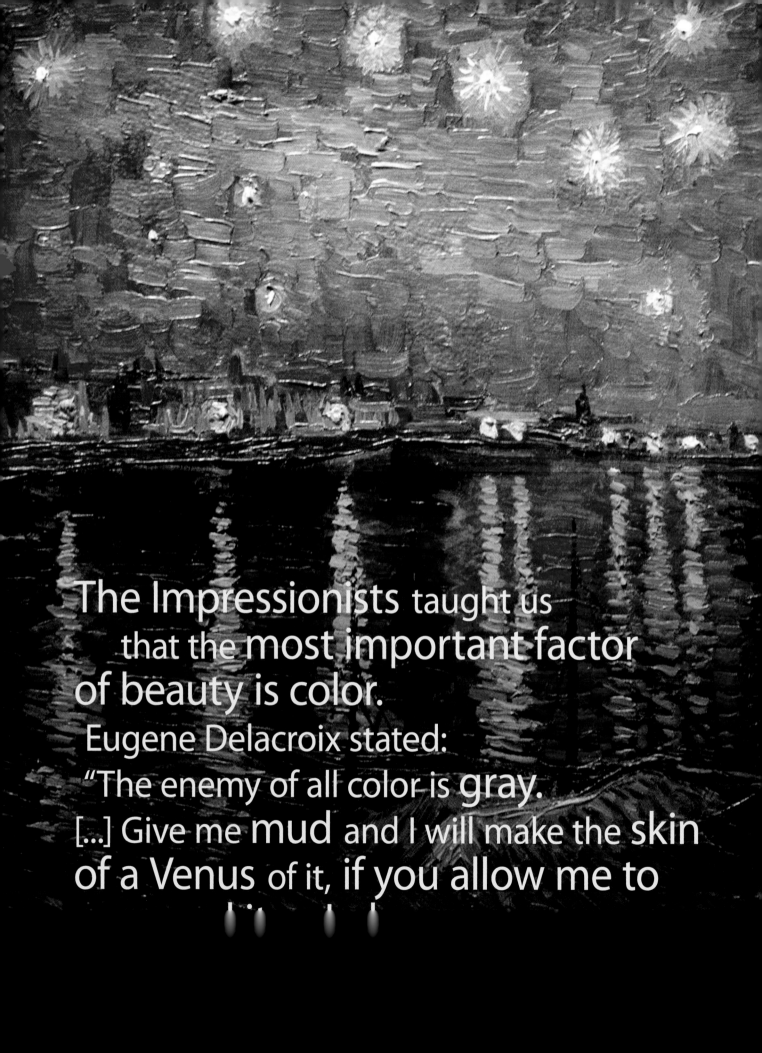

The Impressionists taught us
that the most important factor
of beauty is color.
Eugene Delacroix stated:
"The enemy of all color is gray.
[...] Give me mud and I will make the skin
of a Venus of it, if you allow me to

How Colors We Wear Can Make Us Look Good

O ur color—the color of our hair, skin and eyes—reacts with colors we wear: clothes, makeup, and hair color.

How do colors interact with each other?

What interactions do we find appealing and call beautiful?

What makes some combinations seem unappealing? Your skin's natural color reflects and interacts with whatever color surrounds it. Simply stated, you and I look more striking by wearing colors that positively balance our specific mix of primary colors to complete the vibrations to make light. We look less attractive in colors that throw our individual mix of primary colors into greater imbalance.

Your knowledge of color affects how you use color. This color knowledge empowers you to create a personal and dynamic color signature. Whether or not you understand how color law works, it is always happening. It is color law—principles of science in operation from the beginning of time.

The Impressionists taught us that color is the most important factor of beauty. They abandoned line and used color in bold new ways to achieve their dazzling effects. Their use of color can teach us much in the subtleties of how to combine colors to get different effects.

Ralph Fabri wrote about the importance of understanding how the Impressionists used color in his book, *Color: A Complete Guide for Artists.*

Figure 17

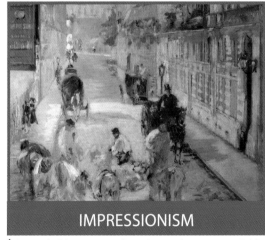

IMPRESSIONISM

Édouard Manet used paint colors to quickly capture the light and figures in his painting, *Road-menders in the Rue Mosnier*, 1878. Notice the absence of strong, distinct lines.

Figure 18

M.E. CHEVREUL

Michel Eugene Chevreul played a prominent role in our current understanding of color.

According to Fabri, "It was the Impressionist school, around the middle of the last century, which discarded lines and decided to work entirely in color."[1] Instead of lines to depict a setting, the Impressionists decided to use color to create images and convey emotions. They were committed to reproducing color as it is optically perceived. The works of Monet, Pisarro, and Van Gogh, as well as the other French Impressionists, introduced the world to a whole new way of understanding formal power—not so much in terms of the shape of a thing as in its color."

MICHEL EUGÈNE CHEVREUL AND THE LAWS OF SIMULTANEOUS CONTRAST

My understanding of how colors in us (our bodies) relate to colors on us (our clothes and cosmetics) came from studying the writings and research of a French chemist and scientist, Michel Eugène Chevreul, who lived and worked just prior to the Impressionist period.

In September 1824, Chevreul was appointed Director of Dyes for the Royal Manufactures, the state-controlled tapestry works at Gobelin, France. This enterprise produced the exquisite tapestry, upholstery, and drapery fabrics that became internationally famous under the patronage of Louis XIV and other French kings. These tapestries graced royal estates throughout Europe.

Chevreul's duties were to oversee the substances used to dye the threads that were then woven into the tapestries. When a color failed to achieve the desired effect, which happened frequently, he concentrated on the problems of dyeing, and therefore on the dyes themselves. It then occurred to him that the main color problems had nothing to do with the chemistry or pigments of the dyes but were more related to optics—the influence of neighboring color tones.[2] In his efforts to improve the quality of colors in the tapestries, Chevreul, who lived 102 years, began a study of color that lasted ten years.

Perhaps his most important discovery was what he called *De la loi du contraste simultane des couleurs,* or *The Principles of Harmony and Contrast of Colors.* He published his article in 1839, which was later translated into English in 1854. In this article, Chevreul defined in precise scientific terms the visual influence of colors in close proximity to one another when viewed at the same time, like the example of the ornaments on the Christmas tree in Chapter Two. Chevreul's scientific experiments determined the effects of color upon all other colors.

Figure 19

THE COLOR LAW

As described in Chapter 2, the red ornaments appear to make the tree more green, while the blue ornaments make it appear less so.

One of Chevreul's most important statements was, "I beg the reader never to forget when it is asserted of the phenomena of simultaneous contrast, that one colour placed beside another receives such a modification from it that this manner of speaking does not mean that the two colours . . . have a mutual action. . . . It is really only applied to the modification that takes place before us when we perceive the simultaneous impression of these two colours."[3] He described his harmony systems as "Harmonie d'analogues," meaning the harmony of analogy or analogous harmony, and "Harmonie de constraste," meaning the harmony of contrasts or complementary harmony.

APPLYING CHEVREUL TO YOU

So how does this relate to you and me? Answer this simple revealing question: "Like Chevreul's challenge in placing tapestry colors, how many times have you worn colors that failed to achieve the desired effect?"

Figure 20

E. DELACROIX

Eugene Delacroix was another great artist of the 19th century.

Reading Chevreul, I realized that his discoveries virtually unlocked the mystery to solve our wearing clothes and cosmetics that either failed or succeeded in achieving our desired effects. Analogous and contrast harmony explain the skin tone interactions that occur with the applied colors of makeup, wardrobe, and a change of hair color. The radiance of our appearance is determined by how the natural hues of our skin interact with the colors of makeup and dress that we apply to us or how our coloring interacts with the colors of the environments that surround us. The principles of analogous and complementary colors set forth by Chevreul explain that interaction.

Among the noted French Impressionists, Eugène Delacroix today is recognized as a "forerunner of the bold technical innovations that strongly influenced the development of Impressionism and subsequent modernist movements."[4] Respected as "the most creative of colorists," he was one of the most influential, "fascinating and complex artistic figures of the 19th century."[5] Delacroix is quoted saying: *The enemy of all color is gray.... Give me mud and I will make the skin of a Venus of it, if you allow me to surround it as I please.*"[6] Chevreul, in his writings, had proved as much.[7]

Are you able to sense, as I did, the importance of that comment? Over and over, I see its applications in our appearances and surroundings.

THE POWER OF COLOR

THE YELLOW ROOM

To hold a three day Success Perceptions Seminar—beauty within and without for women, we booked a large respected hotel in Salt Lake City. The hotel put us in a room wallpapered in citron yellow. That color "muddied" almost everyone's complexion making it impossible to get a correct color profile of our attendees. So what did we do? We took the women in sets of three and four into the nearest bathrooms to get accurate color readings on them. In contrast, the bathrooms had bright, clear light and a soft off-white background which allowed us to clearly see the colors and features of each lady.

"The enemy of all color is gray.... Give me mud and I will make the skin of a Venus of it, if you allow me to surround it as I please." —Delacroix

THE SHOP OWNER

Before I opened my first makeup studio in our local mall, I went to a nearby city to see an existing shop, from the same company, in operation. The studio owner complained to me that business was disappointingly slack; she was anxious for customers. Just then, a woman came into the shop and asked for a makeup consultation. She was rather plain and slightly overweight. Obviously, she felt a need or she wouldn't have come to a makeover studio. A golden opportunity for both women. The customer's coloring was beautifully warm: chestnut hair, rich brown eyes, and golden skin—easily a Red Orange color palette.

The shop owner, not recognizing the woman's natural color temperature, began applying cool makeup colors—pink-toned foundation, blue eyeshadow, and hot pink lipstick. The effect was garish, almost neon. The customer left, apologetically, uncomfortably, without purchasing anything. Both parties felt disappointed and frustrated.

If the shop owner had understood color and had used the right cosmetic colors, this woman would have looked naturally beautiful and, I believe, happily purchased

Figure 21

The gold background is the wrong color for these women. It fades them and robs them of presence.

The right colors present each woman by giving her hair, skin, and eyes more definition.

Figure 21

Figure 22

BEFORE WITHOUT MAKEUP

WITH THE WRONG MAKEUP COLORS

WITH THE RIGHT MAKEUP

Using your correct colors will emphasize your natural beauty, not the current fashion trend or color. Left, you see the young woman without makeup. Middle, you see the young woman's makeup colors first. Right, you see the young woman first. Her makeup supports her rather than detracting from her.

the makeup. By knowing color, the owner could have interacted confidently with all her customers.

Color is law. Color is science. Used correctly, color multiplies our virtues and creates beauty.

THE CARROT-ORANGE HAIR

Sue, a client with carrot-orange hair came into my studio wearing a jarring fuchsia lipstick. She showed me a color collection from another system, which had been prescribed as her color palette. It contained both bright orange and fuchsia.

I set the fuchsia by the orange and said, "Do you like those two colors together?"

"No!" She exclaimed. "They fight each other."

I then asked, "Since your hair is bright orange, how then can you look attractive wearing fuchsia lipstick?"

She nodded as she recognized her new understanding of a simple, logical principal of warm and cool compatibility and incompatibility. Her Beauty Code Color profile put her in the golden Yellow Orange Collection, which she loved. Her new look gathered many compliments.

DISCOVERIES AND CONCLUSIONS

I was thrilled with my new knowledge from Chevreul. In terms of personal attractiveness, the interaction of two colors can cause either harmony or discord. As a result, our use of color will work either for us or against us.

An accurate color system should supply accurate knowledge of how these effects are created. It should teach principles of how to apply that knowledge to control those color effects. This knowledge would give us capability in creating the appearance effect we want. Naturally, we want a different effect on Halloween than we would in going to a formal dance.

As you now think about this, you can see that in understanding skin colors, I could begin to scientifically perceive and define people in color terminology—by their individual portions of the primary colors plus melanin. Then by unlocking the color reactions of analogous and complementary colors, Chevreul allowed me to further understand and define the interaction that takes place between the colors we wear and the natural coloring of our bodies. The system is so logical—so beautifully simple and understandable. It allows us to use color wisely and knowledgeably. We can intensify or subdue our appearance as we choose and always look fabulous. Knowing this, we can always accomplish good effects for ourselves. Think of what that can mean to you and the results you can have. Fabulous.

"Johan Sebastian Bach explained why some music sounds good and why other music doesn't. People then didn't understand this. Bach was the first to identify the principles that made music pleasing, inspiring, exalting–fun. Thus he freed people to compose myriads of music with confidence. That is what Marilyn Starr Harris has done with color."
—*Tonya Stimpson*

SUMMARY

Here is a summary of the principles I learned from Newton, the Impressionists, and Chevreul:

- Light interacts with pigment to create color. An apple, because of its red pigment, rejects red light waves, so red light waves are what our eye perceives and our brain recognizes.

- The three primary colors (red, yellow, and blue), plus melanin, determine the color of our skin.

- Wearing colors will create either harmonious or jarring effects.

- The key to looking your best is to wear the one palette of colors that brings your primary colors into the balance of pure light (by using the analogous and complementary effect of each color). This gives you a natural inviting, captivating radiance. You look and feel wonderful.

- Color is more important than style. Color is more important than line.

I've worked with the Beauty Code Color System religiously since the day you were here and find it's absolutely accurate. I wore my 'new face' for two weeks without changing one item and then put my old makeup on one morning. Good grief! I looked like a painted china doll. I was taught I could wear every color if I simply changed my makeup to match. Not so!"
—*Judith S., interior designer, Menlo Park, CA.*

When we understand the interactions of color against color, we can use color to achieve the appearance effects that we desire.

I now understand why existing beauty color systems did not work for me. They never could. The colors were so mixed in undertones, I could never get a consistent effect. They were not based on the laws of physics that govern the production, the behaviors, nor the interactions of color—of light—the color constant in our world.

Client, René B., "I love the Beauty Code Color system for buying clothes. Sales people tell you the color for this season is purple, gold, or whatever. Once you have Marilyn's book, you never want to try this or that because you know you'll waste your money because you won't look good, you wont like it, and you wont wear it. With the Beauty Code, I know how to be right."

You, like I, can understand the behavior of color so you, like I, can now wear a wide variety of colors within your color range. This will give you a multitude of color effects. You will have vivid colors of strong contrast, subtle pastels that create an ethereal effect, and basic "best" colors you can depend on. You will never worry about how you look because you will know how to look your best—and that is enough.

A sweet granddaughter asked me once, "Grandma, am I the prettiest girl in the world?" "No, Rachel," I replied, "but you are one of the pretty ones." And she is—as are Natasha, Elyse, Meagan, Shelby, Abby, Jaimie, Kaylene, and Sadie Jane.

I say the same to you. Using the laws of color and style, you and every woman can multiply your good features, minimize your imperfections to be one of the pretty ones. I see it every week. Women who care to be exemplary examples of wholeness.

CHAPTER 4 NOTES

[1] Ralph Fabri, *Color: A Complete Guide for Artists* (New York: Watson-Guptill Publications, 1967).

[2] Chevreul's Influence

Because of Chevreul's studies into color vision and color harmony, he became the authoritative Master of Impressionism and Neo-Impressionism, the two schools of painting during his time.

[3] Michel Eugène Chevreul, *The Principles of Harmony and Contrast of Colors and Their Applications to the Arts*, (New York: Van Nostrand Reinhold, 1981) 51.

[4] "Eugène Delacroix." Encyclopaedia Britannica. 2007. Encyclopaedia Britannica Online. 25 Jan. 2007 <http://search.eb.com.erl.lib.byu.edu/eb/article-9029782>.

[5] Ibid.

[6] Faber Birren, "Introduction and Explanatory Notes", *The Principles of Harmony and Contrast of Colors and Their Applications to the Arts*, Michel Eugène Chevreul (New York: Van Nostrand Reinhold, 1981).

[7] Chevreul, *The Principles of Harmony and Contrast of Colors.*

Knowing the science of color
makes life more and less . . .

. . . more fun, more simple,
more secure, and . . .
. . . less stressful, less frustrating,
less confusing.

Knowing Your Best Colors. Why Does it Matter?

chapter 5

Y ou are a being of color . . .
. . . a being of energy, vibration and light
. . . because color is energy, vibration and light.

You have a unique color pattern–an imprint in your hair, skin and eyes that is yours alone. Differences in hair and skin may start at black and move through tones to blondes of the fairest skin. Eye colors may be dark brown to pale blue. Each of us are made to show up in our own certain way.

Whenever we put any color against us, a consistent color reaction takes place. Like children, sometimes these colors fight. Sometimes they get along.

When they get along beautifully–with you, your energy, vibration, and light increase. You look better. You feel better.

When they fight with you, your energy, vibration, and light dim and may even go out which makes you look and feel tired, sick, or edgy.

Color is a universal law that surrounds us every minute. Whether we understand it or not, color law is at work increasing or dimming our light by the colors we choose to wear.

This is why you have clothes in your closet that you never wear and you don't know why. And other clothes you wear over and over and you don't know why.

The Beauty Code™ gives you the only color system anywhere that explains the science of why you choose to wear some clothes over others. With this knowledge, you can know how to always increase your energy, vibration, and light to look and feel better because when you feel better, you live better.

Of all the elements in clothing, color has the most forceful effect on your appearance for either good or bad. If the colors are right, they can emphasize all of your skin's lovely tones and give it a moist, healthy appearance—a softness as if it had been lightly powdered. With the right colors, your hair and eyes are striking and distinct. In contrast, wrong colors will fade your features into drab, lifeless tones. Wrong colors also accent the natural overbalances in your skin tone, which can make your skin look leathery, flushed, drained, and pale; even old. That's the value of knowing your best colors.

The effects of color cannot help but affect your emotions. If a color makes your skin and hair look dead and pasty, you will feel tired and drawn when you wear that color. You may not understand what's causing the feeling. You may not realize that when you wear different colors, you may feel different emotions related to those colors. It's preferable then to wear colors that make you look radiant and alive because that look is transferred into a radiant and alive feeling.

Only one section of the color wheel creates your beauty, because it alone scientifically balances your primary color to light. The other five color sections can destroy your radiance and mute your distinctness by throwing you in a state of even greater imbalance. You have a collection of colors which work together so they coordinate, creating beautiful new, unusual combinations of color. You will soon find that when you buy one item in your right colors, it will work with several other items already waiting in your closet. So unexpectedly you get several new looks whenever you buy something.

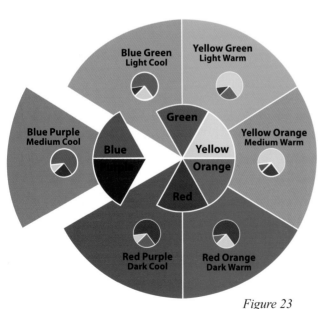

Figure 23

I just referred to "unusual" combinations of color. In the *Beauty Code Color Shopping Guide and Planner* as well as on pages 100 through 105, I've included some striking, "unusual" combinations of color. I "see" them created in attractive, stunning clothes but I never find them in the stores. Because we have not had an accurate system of color, designers design and manufacturers create in "safe" colors —black and white; black, white and red; brown and beige; navy, white and red; red, orange and brown; khaki and tan.

Or designers mix colors from dissonant undertones. Come with me on a buying trip in New York's garment district. I was looking for color coordinated clothing for my store. I remember seeing a gorgeous burgundy print suit. But the designer had designed it with a khaki collar and cuffs. Instinctively, the woman who loved burgundy would be repelled by khaki; the woman who loved khaki would be repelled by burgundy. Walking through designer houses, I repeatedly saw the enormous waste in clothing manufacturing. Not understanding how people instinctively relate to color, designers were creating clothes that customers wouldn't buy.

Johannes Itten, respected German painter, understood the importance of color when he said, "If you, unknowing, are able to create masterpieces in color, then unknowledge is your way. But if you are unable to create masterpieces in color out of your unknowledge, then you ought to look for knowledge."

Also, not understanding the percentage of people in each section of the color wheel, the color leaders in fashion give us cycles of color that don't relate to most people. Just yesterday, a client and associate told a group of us in a meeting, "I hate to go shopping. All I find is gold and orange. I hate gold and orange. I won't wear them. I won't put them in my home."

In working with interior designers, here's what two have told me about doing interiors with my system. Barbara Trish, "This is the only program that has helped me understand each of my clients' individuality. Now I know how to create interiors specifically for them. Knowing where I fit on the color wheel has put me in touch with myself and has opened a new world of color possibilities for me personally."

Marilyn Grayson, "I decorated our whole home myself using my and my husband's color planners. We love our home now. I did it myself so it's our home, our styles, and our personality.

Sometimes you might want to dress in colors different from your collection. You can do that perfectly with The Beauty Code because all Beauty Code Collections are coordinated by undertone. For the perfect effect, plan on adjusting your makeup. You may also have to adjust your hair color because hair color is our most advancing feature.

To get hair colors you love, go to the store or beauty supply house and place the hair color samples, (or the hair colors shown on the box if you're in a drug store), by the palettes of color in the *Beauty Code Color Shopping Guide and Planner*. You can tell quickly which ones work and which don't. In Chapter Nine, I've put together several colors for each Color Category that I know will work for you. I've also outlined how you use them. You can take these directions to your favorite hair colorist or use them yourself.

THE BEAUTY CODE IS KNOWING

In positive or negative impact, we cannot choose whether our lives will be affected by color and style. We can only choose whether we will understand and use the laws that govern those effects.

The Beauty Code™ is knowing, not guessing how to create stunning beauty—a dynamic appearance in yourself. Women love the "knowing."

Knowing saves you time and money. Knowing prevents frustration and stress. Knowing makes the time and money you do spend on color-related decisions more fulfilling. Knowing gives you confidence and makes using color fun!

LIVING SPACES

This same coordination carries over into your living spaces. It's easy to put décor together using your color planner. At my local paint counter, I like to get a few color chips that match the colors in my color planner. Then I experiment with tones and values until the look resonates deeply with me. If the room is for a family member, I start with that family member's personal color planner and involve them in the process. The color plate below shows you proven ways that colors combine to give you many possible color options. They are monochromatic, analogous, complementary, split-complementary, and triad.

WAYS TO COMBINE COLORS

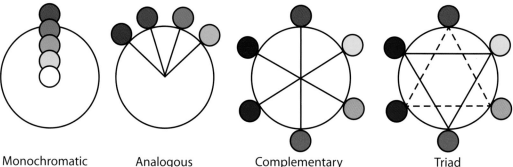

Figure 24   Monochromatic   Analogous   Complementary   Triad

When you decorate an area for public use, know that seventy percent of the population is cool, so decorate mainly in cool or neutral colors. Then add accents of warm colors to help people relax and feel comfortable. For example, when I decorated my hair salon as unisex, I wanted to choose colors that both women and men of all ages could relate to. I chose to use the two most neutral colors on the color wheel—green and red. Opposites. I knew their contrasting effect would create an upbeat mood in the salon. I chose a dark cool evergreen to relate to the cool seventy percent. I knew even the warm color groups would like this green in its darker value.

For accessories, I used brass because the warm brass would reach out to warm color groups and would make the cool color groups feel warm or more at home in that environment. For an accent color, I found a perfect wallpaper of dark green with tiny amounts of clear red to spark interest. I chose a neutral tan carpet and tile. That with lots of green plants, people commented often on how being in the salon felt good—which is just what I wanted to achieve.

Understanding yourself and your best colors opens the door to understanding others and their best colors. This makes gift giving a fun experience rather than an experience of frustration and anxiety. Think about how often you have received a gift you hated from someone you love? You're put in an awful, awkward position of wanting to appreciate them for the gift but not wanting to wear or use the gift because you can't stand it.

A frustrated female voice on my phone said, "Marilyn, I need to bring my husband in for his color profile and I want you to do a spouse consultation. He is always buying me gifts in the wrong colors." She further explained, "It wasn't so bad when it was a bathrobe or a sweater, but he just bought me a new car and I hate the color."

This client and her husband were in opposite Color Palettes. After we determined his right Color Palette, I showed him how he was buying his wife gifts in colors he instinctively loved. Then I showed him her Color Palette and how to take her Color Planner to buy her gifts she loved. Next I showed them how to work their colors together so when they were in their home they each could feel at home in their living spaces. The frustration ended. She now gets gifts in her colors. He finds it easy to give her gifts she loves just as she does for him.

Figure 25

CAROLYN, KARMA, AND SHEILA

From left to right, Carolyn, Karma, and Sheila. Though from the same family and genetics, they each have their own individual colors and look.

Richard Gadd, a long time partner, regularly buys clothing and cosmetics for his wife, Darcus—even lipsticks. He says the knowledge of this color system has made it much more fun to shop for her.

Dear to me are three sisters—Sheila, Carolyn, and Karma. I lived by them growing up. Sheila is among my dearest friends. As different as night and day, each sister has an innate sense of design, which shows up in how they decorate their homes.

All three struggled to find their own identity. The Beauty Code™ Color System used in *Unlocking Your Beauty Code* helped each sister find her right expression and end the struggle.

Sheila and Carolyn are opposites in color; Sheila uses Blue Green–based colors and Carolyn uses Red Orange–based colors. Karma looks best in Blue Purple–based colors, in position next to Sheila on the The Beauty Code Color Wheel.

Carolyn has a very strong sense of herself. A tall, lean and striking brunette, she could be a model. She told me that she never buys anything unless she absolutely loves it. She designs and sews—creating many of her own original outfits because she can control her choices of color and style. Knowing her right colors and lines doubled her confidence as well as her creative expression. "You've kept me beautiful all my life," she recently told me.

Being so close in age, Sheila, influenced by Carolyn's strong statement, wanted to look like her. But Sheila is short and blonde. Fun, friendly, and effervescent, she has a more youthful personality. She loves people and people love her. Her style, her colors, her personality were opposite from Carolyn. I've watched Sheila, forever young, guided by The Beauty Code, create and maintain a fresh, youthful look that is hers alone. Sometimes, the way she puts her colors together simply takes my breath away. She says, "I still love Carolyn's look, but because of The Beauty Code, I know how to pick out the clothes that are right for me."

Marilyn taught me the best colors for me plus the right color of makeup and how to apply it. Now I feel beautiful and know who I am for the first time in my life. —Sheila

The youngest, Karma, sensing the struggle between her two older sisters, felt like an on-looker. She was color-typed "Fall" when she was thirteen, so she tried to wear browns and rusts. "I never felt comfortable," she says, "I felt frumpy and depressed. From that early conditioning, I would never have gone into a store and picked out the Blue Purple–based colors." She was older, married and had a family when she discovered that her best colors were Blue Purple. She says, "It was like coming home. The Beauty Code helped me identify who I was as an individual.

Now I feel comfortable that I look my best. Without The Beauty Code, I don't know that I would have ever discovered it. Where do you go? You can't just go to the store and ask the sales people. They go along with the fashion of the day and let that dictate what you should wear. When I go into a store and pick up lavender, it's like fresh air to my spirit." Carrying a quiet dignity, she continues, "The Beauty Code has given me the tools to be myself. I feel like I finally know me. By knowing my colors through your color system, I feel confident that I look good and I know why."

Understanding color empowers you to use color every day to heighten your mood and achieve the appearance effect that you desire. The marvelous part of The Beauty Code is its scientific base. The color coordinations are already done for you. You don't even need to know how it works. You just need to know that it works and that it can work for you everyday by using your Beauty Code.

You can use this knowledge to successfully buy plants to get the color effects you want in your yard. You can have a vehicle custom designed from your "knowing." You can decorate your office. You can decorate the offices of others from their individuality. Karma used this knowledge to create amazing floral arrangements for the Grand America Hotel in Salt Lake City, Utah.

You have become the best authority on–yourself.

*Understanding yourself and **your** **best** colors opens the door to understanding **others** and their **best** colors*

YOUR APPEARANCE TELLS PEOPLE WHO YOU ARE

Do you look exciting . . .

Because appearance communicates, successful professional women and men have long realized the value of defining and controlling the message they communicate in their appearance. A message of professional and personal confidence is overwhelmingly useful. A silent surface language, your appearance gives clues—indicators about your economic level, your competence and dependability, the direction you're heading, your educational and cultural background. Your appearance can make you look exciting—someone to know—or dull—someone to pass over while looking for someone or something else.

Try this experiment. As you walk down the street, in and out of stores or businesses, mentally put yourself in this position. Imagine that you are an executive conducting job interviews. Qualifications being the same, how do you judge the people you see and meet?

a. Which of these people would you hire as your executive assistant or move up your corporate ladder into management?

b. Perhaps you need a Director of Sales and Marketing. Which of the people you see gives the message you would want given to your clients?

c. If you're a teacher visiting with parents at Parent-Teacher conferences, whose children will you tend to respect more?

d. Which woman or man would you think has the greatest chance of attracting a spouse capable of sharing a healthy and fulfilling long-term relationship rather than one based just on sex appeal?

Notice, you've never met these people, yet you're making judgments about them; their education, their economic status, whether or not you will trust or believe what they would have to say or contribute, where you would place them with confidence—based on what?

Their appearance!

Modern life is fast, contacts are brief, and often we get only one chance to tell another human being who we are. We must make an instant statement. We can't afford to waste an opportunity by sending the wrong signals.

Unfair you think? This question isn't even relevant. Fair or not, it is simply a fact of life. Fight it and we rebel against a reality that sets us up to lose because these judgments affect our lives.

Think about it pragmatically. People spend thousands developing career skills. Businesses spend millions on product development and hundreds of thousands on their image including name, logo, letterhead, literature, and product packaging. They spend millions more on their buildings, decor, front entrance, and working environments. There is, of course, a good business reason for this–image-sensitive packaging and promotion pay big in sales and profit. Personal packaging and promotion pay big in opportunity.

You may have something very significant to contribute. You may represent the best. But if you are packaged poorly, you, like any product, won't sell. Without personal packaging, you most likely won't get the chance to advance. Countless talented people stay bound and boxed–literally left in the warehouse–because they lack appearance and marketing skills. Doesn't it make sense, then, to invest in that part of you that people see and associate with everyday? It's a fact–greater career, social and personal opportunities go to those others who do give serious attention to this part of their personal portfolio.

. . . or ***plain*** *and someone to* ***pass over?***

In *Bridges Out of Poverty*, authors, Payne, Smith, and Devol, explain that clothing is an indicator of economics. Among the poor, clothing is valued for individual style and personality expression. The middle class values clothing for its quality and acceptance into middle class norms. Label is important to the middle class. The wealthy value clothing for its artistic sense of expression. To them, designers are important (pp 44-45, 2006, Process, Inc.).

A form of advertisement, the messages from your appearance are so real that whenever people are confused between your words and your appearance, they believe the message they feel is most authentic–your appearance. You want and need to send out the best possible messages. The good news is no one needs to fail. Every woman and man can learn the rules of color, style, health, grooming, and mannerisms to be attractive.

The Beauty Code™ program of appearance shows you how to send the right signals starting with the radiating presence of wearing the right colors. We teach the skills of appearance appropriate to the goals of each individual.

Figure 26

WHAT ARE YOU COMMUNICATING? WHO OR WHAT DO YOU REPRESENT?

Noted motivational speaker and author Jim Rohn said, "Sophisticated people study consequences."

We all want the consequences of success, happiness, and being thought attractive. Contentment, peace, challenge, acceptance, achievement, and satisfaction—the list is yours to determine and complete. To reach these goals, we need to study consequences. What are the consequences of these following messages?

You cannot not communicate.

And, if you can't communicate, you can't command respect.

We each have a unique and special contribution to make. But with so many voices telling us how to look, what to think, how to eat or not eat, we get confused. My intention is to provide people with simple, straightforward guidelines based on scientific research and studied results—principles. You and anyone can use principles to uncomplicate the physical aspects of our lives.   Right now . . .

What are you communicating?

Who or what do you represent?

The English philosopher and statesman Francis Bacon said, "A good presence and a good fashion carry continual letters of recommendation."

One middle-aged client came to me when her husband was being interviewed for an administrative position at a prestigious university back east. Told that her appearance would weigh positively or negatively in his job interviews, she was concerned. She had never given her appearance much thought because she said, "I didn't want to spend all that time fussing over myself." Although her appearance was plain, she had good features and was very intelligent. She was delighted at how easy it was to find a hairstyle that was correct for her features and easy to keep up. As well, she learned how easily she could apply her makeup properly. She could shop quickly once she knew her correct colors and lines. Her husband did get the job, which was a major step up in his career. And she maintains her appearance because she learned that people respond to her more favorably with her new look.

As Monique progressed through her Beauty Code program, she told me about her friend, a single mother who needed work desperately. She had excellent computer and organizational skills but every time she applied and was interviewed for a job, someone else was chosen. Monique told me of sitting with her while she waited in line for interviews. She said, "I've tried to get her to do something about the way she looks, but she thinks its foolishness. She says people should be able to accept her for what she is. I've seen other women with poorer skills than Jan get the job. I think it's because they look and act better. But, she won't listen to me." I've heard this sad story a lot, haven't you?

Appearance is a mystery to some women and men. They don't even know where to start. Heather felt like that. She was nervous and skeptical about beauty programs. But she had seen such good results with her friends so she was willing to trust my process. Athletic and lean, I knew she wouldn't spend a lot of time on makeup. She didn't need to. Her completed look utilized simple clothes, uncomplicated looks, but when she dressed up she looked well put together—smart, striking. She absolutely loved the fact that she could be casual and still look terrific when she needed or wanted to. To have 'terrific' looks that matched her 'casual' personality was exciting and a relief. Her program showed her how to express facets of her personality she hadn't known existed.

The message of your appearance is controllable.

What you need to control the message of your appearance is the information, the knowledge, the system—The Beauty Code.

Control the **message** *of your* **appearance**

THE PSYCHOLOGY OF COLOR

We live in a world surrounded by color. Color is so basic to life, we use color terms to refer to items around us: a red book, a navy couch, a silver car. Color is language. Color is mood. Color is emotion—your emotion. Psychologically, color can send a positive or negative message, encourage or discourage sales, calm or agitate a conversation.

Colors affect us when we wear them. Colors we wear affect others when they see us. This is because different colors speak their own message. People feel these messages . . . and respond. So it's fun—and important—to know the different messages colors speak.

Let's explore how colors affect us.

Everyone can wear every color if that color is the right undertone. You have versions of each of these colors in your color palette. I arrange my closet by putting like colors together. My blue, pink, green, navy, and more sit together so it's easy to speak the mood I want to express when I dress.

To speak well, any color deserves good fabric. Poor fabrics don't hold up well. Many sag, bag, and cling. Colors fade. Consider this when you choose your clothing or furniture. Having better quality and fewer items will give you more years of good wear and well-spoken messages.

How you mix colors also speaks your personality message with that outfit.

Drama—sharp contrasts of color like black and white, black and red, orange and blue.

Feminine Colors—pastels or cool colors, watercolors effects.

Classic Business—darks with lights and pastels or lights. Avoid brights if you want to be taken seriously.

Classic Casual—dark or medium tones mixed.

Sophisticate—usually muted, dark or light tones used simply with simple jewelry.

Fun activities—brights, in summer with white or tan.

WARM COLORS

Yellow, orange and red stimulate and energize the senses. Restaurants use them because they increase hunger.

COOL COLORS

Blue, purple, and green calm, relax, and allow sophistication.

DARK COLORS

Serious in nature, they're "down to business colors" that convey authority and respect. They say that the wearer is focused on the work at hand "outside themselves

No-nonsense, dark colors are practical because they don't show soil. Use dark colors for three seasons of the year—fall, winter, and spring—because they form a solid, practical backbone to your wardrobe.

DARK FASHION COLORS

These include any dark color. For example, dark versions of red and purple take in burgundy, grape or eggplant; greens—evergreen, khaki or moss; browns and grays—chocolate, walnut or charcoal. You get the idea. These colors convey a more formal message than light or bright colors. You begin your signature statement when you use your dark colors as core wardrobe colors. They combine successfully with almost if not all of your other colors, so automatically you're speaking a personal message.

BLACK

Positive responses, messages, and/or effects:

Black stands for authority, power, a serious, no-nonsense focus. Black invites respect, but if overused or used in the wrong situations, black can be intimidating. Black represents sophistication, sexuality, wealth, fear, anonymity, remorse, anger, and death. Black is the absence of light therefore the absence of color. Used in a cosmetic case, black features all colors better than white.

"In the black" means the business is financially sound. A karate black belt means the highest level of karate expertise. A black tie event is the most formal. In fashion, black denotes sophistication, elegance and fashion savvy. Black makes you look thinner but also outlines every figure flaw in your silhouette.

Negative color responses, messages, and/or effects:

Black represents secrecy, grief, and mourning in Europe and America. Black is the color of night, evil, mystery, and intimidation. Villains wear black. People tend to feel inconspicuous when they wear black.

Using too much black intimidates and overwhelms.

Think of these negative meanings that we attach to black.

Color can **speak** *your mood even* **change** *your mood*

Black listed—to exclude or avoid. Blackguard, a scoundrel; black sheep, an outcast. Blackmail, using threat to get gain; black market, illegal trade in goods or money. A black out is a time period of darkness without electricity either from power outages or for air raid protection. When you black out, you lose consciousness temporarily. Black humor is morbid, unhealthy, gloomy humor. Think of 'black cats' and 'black Mondays' on Wall Street.

NAVY

Navy speaks the same messages as black, but with less intensity and therefore less intimidation.

BROWN

Positive responses, messages, and/or effects:

Reliable, stabile, and friendly, brown stabilizes us physically and mentally. Genuine, wholesome, and earthy, brown gives us a sense of order, of being 'grounded.' Because it's the color of earth, brown is one of the color constants of our world, natural, organic—a masculine color. Think of dark brown woods and leathers. Warm color palettes use brown as the cool color palettes use black and navy.

Negative color responses, messages, and/or effects:

Brown can be sad, wistful, boring, nondescript especially if you're a cool color palette because it's not one of your best colors.

NEUTRALS

Consists of white, winter white, creams, beiges, tans, and grays.

Sophisticated, neutrals speak class and savvy chic. Their simplicity gives them elegance and drama especially for evening wear. Warm color palettes use tans and creams for their summer wardrobe basics.

WHITE

Positive responses, messages, and/or effects:

White gives the highest message of integrity and purity.

People who wear cool colors (Blue Purple, Red Purple, Blue Green) like white for their summer wardrobe. It denotes integrity, purity, cleanliness, and excellent character. A white knight is a rescuer. A white room is a clean room, temperature-controlled, and dust free for precision instruments. White heat indicates a state of intensity, be it anger, devotion, enthusiasm, or passion. White garments can mean purity (as in marriage), good luck, or sophistication. White represents the transparency and safety of bright or full light. Absence of color projects neutrality. White aids mental clarity and promotes pure thoughts and actions. Represents new beginnings the opportunity to clear clutter and obstacles. We depict angels in white.

Negative color responses, messages, and/or effects:
Whited sepulcher denotes a person who appears 'pure' or of integrity on the surface but is inside an evil hypocrite. To white wash is to gloss over defects or make something appear better than it is. A white out is the blizzard's zero visibility. In eastern cultures, people associate white with mourning.

GRAY
Positive responses, messages, and/or effects:
High sophistication of Banker's Gray represents 'the Institution.' Gray speaks a practical, solid, timeless, moderate and no-nonsense message.

Negative color responses, messages, and/or effects:
Negative meanings include death, decay, and depression. We associate gray with old age, loss, sorrow, lack of life, 'gray' areas that lack full understanding and a lost sense of direction.

TANS/CREAMS
Tans/Creams as warm neutrals give a more relaxed, inviting and softer sense that gray and cream—less formal, and more casual.

PASTELS
Positive color messages, responses, and/or effects:
Most pastels feel calm and restful. When you wear them, you're more approachable so they're good colors to wear for counseling, sales, and medical uniforms. Most common are tones of cool colors—green, blue, lilac, and pink but all colors have a pastel version and can combine in unusual ways.

Negative color responses, messages, and/or effects:
Pastels lack strength and dynamic energy. They can be lifeless.

BRIGHT COLORS
Positive color messages, responses, and/or effects:
Good for training, teaching, sports, and evening wear. Bright colors exert a creative influence that psychologically stimulates the mind and intellect.

Negative color responses, messages, and/or effects:
Can excite inappropriate energy causing too much stimulation, too much attention—can overwhelm.

Pastels
are
peaceful

RED

Positive color messages, responses, and/or effects:

Red, a strong, slow wave, gives us the highest emotional response of any of the colors. Red attracts the most attention. Because red is so visible and impacting, we use it for stop signs, stop lights, brake lights, fire equipment, and emergency vehicles. Red means passion, patriotism, anger; both love and hate. You can alter its meaning by what you put with it, i.e. with a navy suit, white shirt, it's patriotic in America. With white or pink and orange, it's festive. With black, it can be elegant and even sinister. White, navy and red was chosen by IBM as the wardrobe colors for their sales and executives because white stands for integrity; navy for stability and responsibility; red for energy, passion, and patriotism.

If you wear red when firing someone or giving criticism, it becomes harsh. Red encompasses scarlet and crimson, pink and burgundy. Red increases enthusiasm, stimulates energy, encourages action, exudes confidence, and gives people a sense of courage and protection from fears and anxiety.

Red means love, giving, and festivity at Christmas, Valentine's and other times when we "paint the town red" to celebrate. We associate red with aggression and strength which is why most countries worldwide use red in their national flags. Energetic, we associate red with movement and excitement. Hearts beat faster in red rooms; some feel out of breath.

Negative color responses, messages, and/or effects:

You're noticed more and appear heavier in red clothes. Red cars get more tickets either because they're more noticeable or drivers drive faster in a red car—perhaps both. We "see" red when we're angry. A red herring distracts our attention away from the real issue. "In the red," finances are losing money. Too much red over stimulates and will heighten aggression.

BURGUNDY

Burgundy, a version of red, expresses quality, high class, and good taste.

PINK

Derived from red, pink speaks the true color of love and said by some to be the most calming of all colors. Because pink drains energy and calms aggression, prisons house dangerous criminals in pink cells. Sports teams put their opponents in pink locker rooms before sports events.

BLUE

Positive color messages, responses, and/or effects:

Blue represents peace, tranquility, stability, harmony, unity, and trust. We use blue to symbolize qualities like truth, calm, confidence, dependability, conservatism, steadfastness, commitment, security, cleanliness, order, and loyalty.

Consider these blue phrases: "true blue," "feeling blue," "out of the blue," "into the blue" (or the unknown). Blue book and blue blood denote people who are socially prominent or of noble descent. It has been suggested that these two terms maybe linked to aristocrats who first used this term.

A blue ribbon is first place; a blue ribbon panel is a group of highly qualified people. Blue laws enforce moral standards; a "blue nose" describes a strict, puritanical person.

The color of sky and water, blue is one of the constant colors of life. It's often used to represent technology. Blue can slow a pulse rate, lower body temperature, and reduce your appetite.

Because blue calms and expresses trust and reliability, it's used for clothes in business, sales and law enforcement. Fashion consultants recommend wearing blue for job interviews. It is the safest color to wear globally because it's the overwhelming "favorite color" of women and men. It's cooling to wear and aids intuition. People are most productive in blue rooms. Electric and brilliant blues create dramatic, dynamic effects as in a peacock or kingfisher's feathers.

Negative color responses, messages, and/or effects:

Overused, blue can feel cold, lifeless, sterile, and uncaring. While a favorite color in clothes and decor, blue is rare in nature and unappetizing in food because it denotes spoiled or toxic food. Too much blue can trigger depression.

PURPLE

Positive color messages, responses, and/or effects:

Purple embodies the balance of red stimulation and blue calm. Our most royal color, it's the classic robe color for kings and queens. Purple means wealth and prosperity. It takes on the characteristics of its undertone either red purple or blue purple, so it can stimulate or calm accordingly. Purple expresses rich sophistication, wisdom, respect, and feminine, romantic qualities.

Control your color messages

We're charmed by the mystic and mysterious qualities of purple. Leonardo da Vinci believed purple light increased the power of meditation ten times more than normal. He liked to meditate in the purple light of stained glass. Richard Wagner composed his operas in a room decorated in shades of violet, his "color of inspiration." It's believed that children develop more imagination in a purple room. I wonder how this connects with purple being the color of the chakra at the top of the head? Teen girls tend to prefer lavender.

Green ***soothes*** *and* ***relaxes mentally***

Negative color responses, messages, and/or effects:
Purple, too, can be overpowering, either over stimulating or depressive depending on whether you use a red purple like wine or a blue purple like periwinkle.

GREEN
Positive color messages, responses, and/or effects:
A repeat "favorite" color, green means nature, environment, health, good luck, renewal, youth, growth, money, vigor, spring, generosity, and fertility. Good gardeners have a "green" thumb. Another "constant" color of our natural world, greens from forest to lime give feelings of tranquility and refreshment. Men like dark, forest green and many green shades in general. A "cool" unsophisticated color, green calms and supports healing so surgeons often wear green operating clothes—the after effect color from seeing red. Because green soothes and relaxes mentally, it's used to alleviate depression, nervousness and anxiety. It offers a sense of renewal, self-control and harmony. It's the easiest color on the eyes and can improve vision. "Green backs" are US dollars. Performers relax in a "Green Room" before going on TV, the stage of the concert hall or theater.

Negative color responses, messages, and/or effects:
Jealousy, the "green-eyed monster," or "green" with envy. Conversely it means inexperienced, youthful, naive as in being "green" or a "greenhorn" and so is often associated with misfortune as well as fortune. Green associations include illness, "green behind the gills," slime, or bilious conditions.

"The Beauty Code System works if people will continually use it. It answers all the questions people have. You can prove it. It gives me more freedom. I can use all of the tints, tones and shades in my colors for more variety. I can create moods with what color represents."
—Sherry Jacobson, makeup artist,

ORANGE
Positive color messages, responses, and/or effects:
A combination of yellow and red, orange is a warm color like red, but not as intense. Fun and flamboyant, orange encourages socialization, activity, and appetite. Energetic, orange has luminous qualities that gather attention.

Orange brings up fond memories of fall with its brilliant leaves, pumpkins, and Halloween. This vibrant color symbolizes balance, warmth, enthusiasm, and flamboyancy. Its tones of terra cotta, peach, or rust have broad appeal. We associate orange with ambition and the dawn of a new attitude.

Negative color responses, messages, and/or effects:
Overpowering, overbearing, overwhelming, sparks more controversy than any other color. People either love or hate orange. It can easily look cheap.

YELLOW

Positive color messages, responses, and/or effects:
Cheerful, sunny, and optimistic; yellow catches our attention. It's associated with laughter, happiness, and good times. Mentally stimulating, yellow means enlightenment and improves concentration hence yellow legal writing pads. Yellow speeds up metabolism and stimulates the nervous system. It activates memory and enlivens and encourages conversation. Yellow ribbons show support for troops. It's intimately connected with peace and well being. Golden tones mean good times, even wealth. Used as an accent color in small amounts, yellow can add spark to a room, in clothes, and packaging or advertisements to improve sales. Highly visible, yellow warns people as in quarantine, crime scenes, and construction sites.

Negative color responses, messages, and/or effects:
Yellow over stimulates the senses so people argue more and babies cry more in rooms painted or decorated with yellow furniture. We refer to cowardly people as yellow or having a yellow streak. Yellow symbolizes jealousy and deceit. Yellow journalism refers to irresponsible and alarmist reporting. People can't look at yellow for long periods of time.

Yellow
activates
memory

Color
has
meaning

WHITE

Ancient Greece—the people wore white to bed to ensure pleasant dreams
Ancient Egypt—Pharaohs wore white crowns
Ancient Persians—believed all gods wore white
Eastern cultures—coldness and sterility
Japan—white carnations signify death
India, Thailand, Burma, and Sri Lanka—a "white elephant" is a rare, pale elephant and is considered sacred.

BLACK

Ancient Egyptians believed black cats had divine powers. They and the Romans used black for mourning just as we do today.

RED

The Ancient Egyptians considered themselves a red race and painted their bodies with red dye for emphasis.
Russia—red means beautiful. The Bolsheviks used a red flag as their symbol when they overthrew the Czar in 1917. This is how red became the color of communism.
India—red is the symbol for a soldier. It's also the color of purity and is used for wedding clothing.
South Africa—red is the color of mourning.
China—red is the color of good luck and celebration. It's used as a holiday, wedding, and funeral color. Chinese babies are given their names at a red-egg ceremony.
Greece—eggs are dyed red for good luck at Easter time.
England—during the English War of the Roses, red was the color of the House of Lancaster, which defeated the House of York, symbolized by the color white.
Italy—the "Redshirts" were the soldiers of the Italian leader Garibaldi, who unified modern Italy in the nineteenth century.

BLUE

Ancient Rome—public servants wore blue. Today, police and other public servants still wear blue.
Iran—blue is the color of mourning.
Ancient Egypt—Pharaohs wore blue for protection against evil.
China—blue is associated with immorality.
Colombia—blue is associated with soap.
India—for Hindus, blue is the color of Krishna.
Israel—for Jews, blue symbolizes holiness.
Middle East—blue is a protective color.

PURPLE

Egypt–Queen Cleopatra loved purple. To obtain one ounce of Tyrian purple
dye, she had her servants soak 20,000 Purpura snails for ten days.

Thailand–purple is worn by a widow mourning her husband's death.

GREEN

Libya–the only national flag of a solid green color.

Ancient Egypt—they colored the floors of their temples green.

Ancient Greece—green symbolized victory.

Scotland—people wore green as a mark of honor.

Ireland— tied to the color of the shamrock, green is Ireland's national
color and has religious significance for Catholics.

China—green hats mean a man's wife is cheating on him; it is not a good
color choice for packaging either.

India—green is the color of Islam.

Some tropical countries associate green with danger.

ORANGE

Ireland–orange has religious significance for Protestants.

YELLOW

Egypt and Burma–yellow signifies mourning.

Spain—executioners once wore yellow.

India—yellow is the symbol for a merchant or farmer.

France—during the tenth century, the doors of traitors and criminals were
painted yellow.

India—Hindus wear yellow to celebrate the festival of spring.

Japan—during the War of Dynasty in 1357, each warrior wore a yellow
chrysanthemum as a pledge of courage.

Middle Ages—actors portraying the dead in a play wore yellow.

An **exercise** to **choose**
your best colors of **light**,
and **personal beauty**

Your Personal Color
Code Discovery

Welcome to the most exciting color discovery of our time—a discovery in a personal color system unlike any color system you've ever experienced. A color system that will give you the results it promised. You will look stunning and have greater presence. Every color decision you make will be correct. You can become your own best color authority.

With this color system, you will choose the right cosmetic color every time. No more drawers bursting with unused cosmetics. No more lipstick and foundation colors that change on you. No more clothes in your closet that you never wear because they don't look or feel right. Waste is gone.

This Beauty Code Color System shows you your correct colors and the correct methods of using those colors. You will learn how the system works so you have confidence in using color.

Your clothes will combine in new and exciting ways. You will experience shopping success for yourself and others. You will choose correct colors for gifts that please them, decorate rooms that help them feel settled and content, help them dress in colors that build their confidence and sense of well being—just as you will do the same for yourself.

The Beauty Code Color System is based on the principles of light. As surely as you can trust the colors of the prism to never change, you can trust this system, because it is not based on hype or gimmick. You can use it again and again to control color in all its variety, through every degree of its complexity. The source of all life, light is a true and enduring principle. You can rely on the Beauty Code Color System because it alone relies on the science of light.

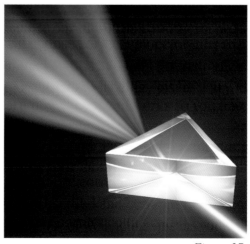

Figure 27

A SCIENCE OF PERSONAL COLOR

The Beauty Code Color System is a historical breakthrough. Since time began, this is the first time anyone has broken the code of the Science of Personal Color. Until now, we've been told we get our personal color from incomplete color science, gimmick, or hype. To understand this, look at the other color systems available at the end of this chapter.

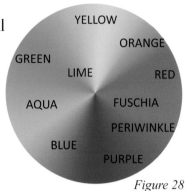

Figure 28

THE BEAUTY CODE COLOR SYSTEM

The color wheel developed by Marilyn Starr Harris provides the foundation of her Beauty Code Color System. Marilyn's color wheel is turned to a new position; green rather than yellow on top, red rather than purple on the bottom. Every person fits into one of six color collections. Light toned people will fit into one of the four collections at the top of the color wheel. Dark toned people will fit into one of the bottom four color collections.

Figure 29

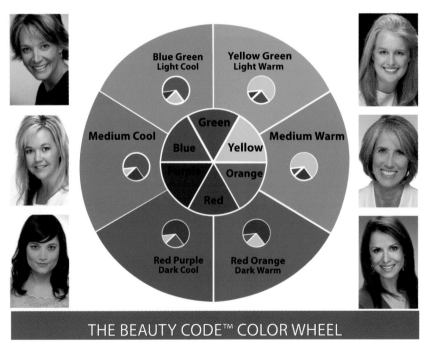

THE BEAUTY CODE™ COLOR WHEEL

Like Sir Isaac Newton's color wheel, which is based on the Science of Light (Optics), Marilyn's Color Wheel addresses the four main elements of color: hue, temperature, value, and intensity. It gives us a scientific constant.

Hue–the name or tone of all colors found in prisms or rainbows. The Beauty Code Color Wheel includes all primary, secondary, and tertiary colors. Each collection offers every color blended in the right undertones. This is why all colors in each collection coordinate and harmonize so completely.

Temperature–with green at the top and red at the bottom, Marilyn's color wheel divides equally into a warm side (yellow and orange) and a cool side (blue and purple). While red is warmer than green, both green and red change temperature more easily than other colors. Green and red both become warm by mixing them with yellow and cool by mixing them with blue. For example, red with yellow added becomes rust (warm); with blue added, red becomes burgundy (cool). Green with yellow added becomes lime (warm); with blue added green becomes emerald (cool). Orange and yellow can never become cool; blue and purple can never become warm.

Value–value is maintained for people i.e. blondes (light), brownettes (medium) and brunettes (dark), warm or cool, each fit into either a warm or cool collection of colors.

Intensity–All collections include bright, strong, pastel, dull, or muted intensities of color.

YOUR INSTINCTS ABOUT COLOR
You have instincts about your best colors.

To get a sense of your instinct for color go to your closet and sort your clothes into two groups, your favorites and clothes you rarely or don't like to wear. What colors are in your "keep" pile, –in your 'toss' pile? Are they warm or cool colors? Write those down.

You will find your good colors are in the group of clothes you naturally wear more often and the bad colors you naturally wear less often, or never.

Let me give you some examples of personal preference being overridden by other forces. As a child, I was drawn to purples and violets. But I was told that "purple is a harsh color–difficult to wear," so I avoided wearing shades of purple. In truth, violets and purples are among my best colors. Research, knowledge of color, and experience have finally put me back in touch with my instincts.

My friend Susie, when young, loved a gold car in her neighborhood. She looked for it everyday. Once, driving her to school, her father commented,

"Why would anyone buy a car in that hideous color?" Susie felt instantly shamed with her color preference and thereafter avoided gold—one of her best colors. As she had red, or "gold" hair, her father's comment made her wonder if she too was a "hideous color" and ugly.

Several decorators told me, "brown carpet matches with anything." This conditioning resulted in expensive let downs. I made brown decorating decisions that were boring, even disturbing for my husband and me. Now we enjoy a royal purple carpet.

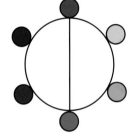

Figure 30

Your instincts haven't given you all your best colors for two reasons. First, a complete and accurate system of personal color has not existed to guide you until now. Personal color systems have been based on gimmick, hype, and incomplete information, so we're confused. Second, your instincts about color are often covered by conditioning from those around you and by fashion.

What is the relationship of personal instinct to scientific principle? I find they reinforce each other. We instinctively like colors that make us look good. But, these instincts are subtle impressions—easily overridden by conditioning comments from others, wanting to imitate a striking color we see on another person, or following the colors featured in a current fashion cycle whether right for us or not.

RIGHT COLORS WILL:
- Blend naturally with your own coloring, creating a lift to your appearance— literally as if your face lifts up and moves forward an inch or two. You to see yourself first, not the color.

- Blend your natural coloring (skin, hair, and eyes) with the colors put next to you so the colors create a circle of harmony with you.

- Make hair, brows, and lashes appear more distinct. Blonde hair will appear lighter with more radiant highlights to frame the face. Brownette hair looks richer, and brunette hair has more depth and intensity.

- Make your skin take a secondary role, supporting the hair and eye color rather than dominating them. Skin will look creamed, blended in color, softly moist, or as if lightly powdered, radiant and alive.

WRONG COLORS WILL:
- Put a cast of gray or yellow over your skin, an anemic or ruddy tone.

- Pull your face down into the color by intensifying the dark lines in the face. This will make you look tired and older.

- Form a line between the color and your natural coloring. Wrong colors "sit" on you and jump out to be noticed. You will see the color first, not you. The color on you conflicts with the color you are.

THE BEAUTY CODE COLOR COLLECTIONS

The next sixteen pages outline the Beauty Code Color System, the Color Collections with Color Coordinations for each collection.

7 STEPS TO FIND YOUR BEST COLORS

1. Note your instincts about color. Sort your clothes into two piles, "keep" or "toss." What colors are in your "keep" pile, –in your 'toss' pile? Are they warm or cool colors?

2. What colors do you instinctively choose for random items like tissue boxes or broom handles? Remember favorite colors from your childhood. Do you instinctively choose warm or cool colors? ☐ Warm ☐ Cool

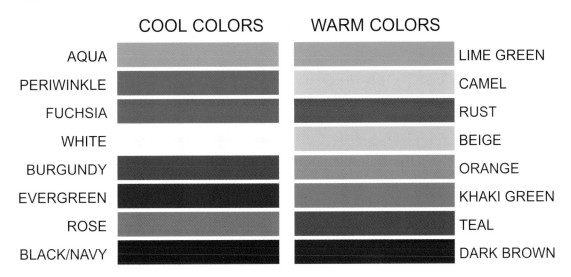

COOL COLORS	WARM COLORS
AQUA	LIME GREEN
PERIWINKLE	CAMEL
FUCHSIA	RUST
WHITE	BEIGE
BURGUNDY	ORANGE
EVERGREEN	KHAKI GREEN
ROSE	TEAL
BLACK/NAVY	DARK BROWN

3. Look at pages 92-99 to find your natural hair color (ages 12–22).

4. Ask yourself which two colors of the colors that follow do you like best, and which two do you like least? Red, Yellow, Blue, Green, Orange, and Purple.
Best Two:_____ Least Two _____

Are your best colors warm or cool? Are you least favorite colors warm or cool?

Which of your favorite colors do you find in the collections named in Step 5?

5. Look at the color collections on pages 94-99 and ask yourself, "If I had to live with one color collection for the rest of my life, which would I choose?"

My best Beauty Code Color Collection is:

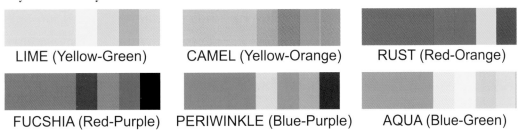

LIME (Yellow-Green)   CAMEL (Yellow-Orange)   RUST (Red-Orange)

FUCSHIA (Red-Purple)   PERIWINKLE (Blue-Purple)   AQUA (Blue-Green)

6. To be sure you get your best colors, follow this step carefully. If you are choosing between:

It ***feels*** *good to wear* ***your best colors***

a. Aquamarine–Blue Green or Peridot–Yellow Green:
  - If you prefer turquoise (turquoise jewelry) and coral, you're Blue Green.
  - If you prefer peach/soft orange and lime green, you're Yellow Green.

b. Peridot–Yellow Green or Topaz–Yellow Orange:
  - If you prefer peach/soft orange and lime green, you're Yellow Green.
  - If you love camel, khaki, and orange, you're Yellow Orange.

c. Topaz–Yellow Orange or Garnet–Red Orange:
  - If you love camel, khaki, and orange, you're Yellow Orange.
  - If you prefer rust, brown, and goldenrod yellow, you're Red Orange.

d. Garnet–Red Orange or Ruby–Red Purple:
  - If you prefer rust, brown, and goldenrod yellow, you're Red Orange.
  - If you love purple and black, you're Red Purple.

e. Sapphire–Blue Purple or Ruby–Red Purple:
  - If you prefer navy blue, you're Blue Purple.
  - If you prefer black, you're Red Purple.

f. Sapphire–Blue Purple or Aquamarine–Blue Green:
  - If you prefer blue denim and love pink, you're Blue Purple.
  - If you prefer turquoise (turquoise jewelry) and coral, you're Blue Green.

7. To discover your best color intensity, try the following color intensities on you in front of the mirror: colors that are pastel, bright, muted, dark, and rich jewel tones. People with clear, radiant skin look amazing in pastels. People with mottled skin tones look best in muted, rich colors. My best color intensities are: ☐ Bright ☐ Muted ☐ Pastel ☐ Dark Rich

Colors to Avoid: Avoid wearing colors in the other five color collections, especially those in the 3 color collections opposite you on the color wheel. Opposite colors throw you into greater states of color imbalance. See Wrong Colors pg. 88.

It took me over a year to put the colors in each collection together so they would balance the unique pigment code of those people in that part of the color wheel. Now you have a beauty system based on science so accurate and so easy to follow you can create your most beautiful appearance every day as if a professional did your makeup, hair, and outfit.

GRAY HAIR

Hair grays differently according to the coloring in the Color Collections: Blue Purple, Blue Green, and Yellow Green have variations of pure white or creamy white hair; Red Purple become salt and pepper then white; Yellow Orange and Red orange—a variety of lightest beige tones.

COLOR AND AGE

As we age, our color intensity and value will change but never in hue and temperature. Young, clear skin and hair respond to light, clear, and bright colors. In our twenties, usually as we marry and bear children, hormone changes occur that darken our coloring. Then rich, dark, or muted colors look good. With age and wrinkles, softer colors look better because dark colors spotlight the dark lines in the face.

COLOR INTENSITY

You each have preferred color intensities. Some of you look best in colors that are bright; others look best in colors that are muted. Some look heavenly in pastels; others look dynamic in dark rich colors. Look in the mirror and choose which intensities work best for you. Some people have clear, luminous skin; they look best in pastel or bright colors. Others with mottled skin tones look best in muted, rich colors.

SKIN COLOR

Before I understood the science of color, I researched through innumerable books to understand skin tones. Depending on the author, skin was described as tawny, ruddy, pink, alabaster, tan, black, and caramel among others. Now that I understand color science, I think of skin tones in percentages of red, yellow, blue, and black. It's much more accurate. Compatible pigment codes tie your skin and natural hair color together. When I know your right hair color, I understand your skin color and how to mix makeup foundation colors to match it.

EYE COLOR

Eye colors vary quite a bit. I've seen cool brown or warm brown eyes and cool or warm blue eyes. I don't depend on eye color to determine someone's best colors. Eye color will tie to the colors in a person's natural hair color and skin tone.

When Georgia, an attractive Beauty Code Consultant, first discovered her best colors were Garnet–Red Orange, she immediately bought an oversized goldenrod sweatshirt. She said, "I didn't take it off for three days, it felt so good to wear that color." When her friend, Vickie, next saw her, Vickie exclaimed, "Whatever you've found to look like that, I want it too."

Vickie, too, was in the Garnet–Red Orange Collection. After wandered in a color no-man's land for years, she was thrilled to find her best colors. Only The Beauty Code has defined the Garnet Red Orange and the Peridot–Yellow Green Collection.

COOL COLORS

RUBY RED PURPLE	SAPPHIRE BLUE PURPLE	AQUAMARINE BLUE GREEN

Brunette

light

medium

dark

dark
(includes all ethnicities)

Brownette

light

medium

dark

Brunette

light

Blonde

light

medium

dark

Blonde

light

medium

dark

Strawberry Blonde

medium light

Figure 31

PERIDOT
YELLOW GREEN

Blonde

light

Redhead

light

medium

TOPAZ
YELLOW ORANGE

Blonde

medium

Brownette

dark

Red

light auburn

GARNET
RED ORANGE

Brownette

light

Redhead

medium auburn

dark

dark auburn

Brunette

medium

dark

dark

Because your hair is so close to your face, it affects your complexion. Wrong hair color washes you out. The right hair color makes your skin look healthy and radiant. This is why people stress over getting the "right" hair color.

Aquamarine
BlueGreen

Stars: Goldie Hawn, Heather Locklear, Kate Hudson, Cate Blanchette

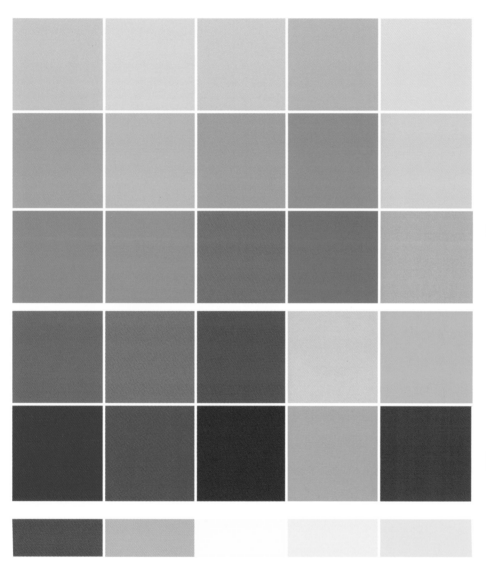

Core: Cool tan, navy
Neutralized: Dusty versions of aqua, coral, green
Pastel: White wool, cream, lightest coral, or aqua
Fun Blue Green Color Coordinations: Dusty aqua with dusty pink or coral; emerald with aqua; coral with yellow; cream with red; aqua with lilac and coral; celery with coral and yellow
Accent: Hot coral, hot aqua, lilac, red, daffodil yellow, green apple, emerald

Metals: Light gold

Core Colors: Dark or neutralized colors that combine well with your other colors for suits, leathers, pants, sweaters, blouses, dresses, jackets
Pastels: Lightest version of any of your colors to use for stationery, china, linens, housewares, business cards
Coordinating Colors: Colors that work well with your core colors to give richness and life to your wardrobe.
Accent Colors: High vibrant colors, vivid, dramatic, sparkling; they give magnetic flair and fun to either formal or sports clothes

Sapphire
BluePurple

Stars: Princess Diana, Jennifer Aniston, Martha Stewart

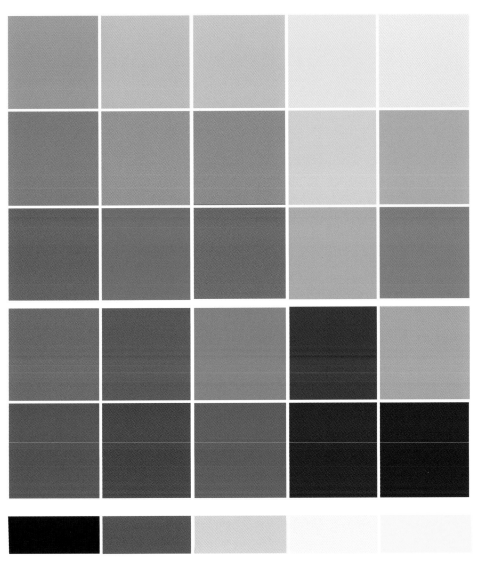

Core: Navy, deep wisteria, lapis, burgundy, cool taupe

Neutralized: Muted periwinkle, denim blue, dusty rose, woodland green, dusty mauve

Pastels: Lightest mauve, pink, white

Intriguing Blue Purple Color Coordinations: Any of the bright, rich versions of your colors, navy with periwinkle and mauve; cornflower blue or woodland green with pale yellow; soft blue with woodland green; hot pink with pansy

Accent: Any hot pink or purple, red, periwinkle, sapphire

Metals: Silver, platinum, light gold

Core Colors: Dark or neutralized colors that combine well with your other colors for suits, leathers, pants, sweaters, blouses, dresses, jackets

Pastels: Lightest version of any of your colors to use for stationery, china, linens, housewares, business cards

Coordinating Colors: Colors that work well with your core colors to give richness and life to your wardrobe

Accent Colors: High vibrant colors, vivid, dramatic, sparkling, they give magnetic flair and fun to either formal or sports clothes

Ruby
RedPurple

Stars: Angelina Jolie, Katie Holmes, Oprah Winfrey

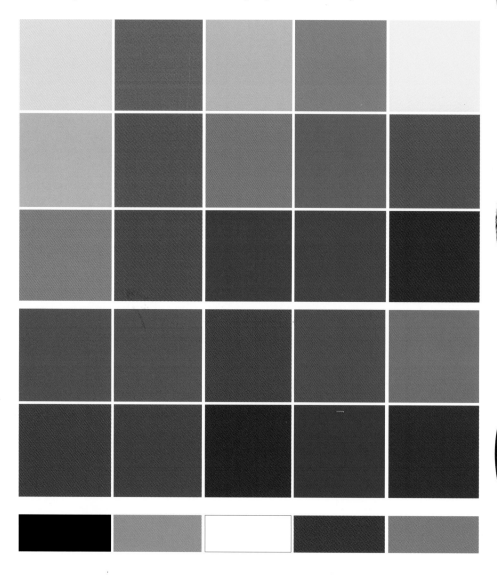

Core: Black, wine, grape, ultramarine, eggplant
Neutralized: Dusty versions of any of your purple, red purples, or blues
Pastel: white, silver, lightest versions of any of your colors including gray
Commanding Red Purple Color Coordinations: Black with dark brown and taupe; eggplant with raspberry; ultramarine blue with amethyst; ivy green with one of your light blues or taupe; plum with fuchsia; black with white and yellow
Accent: Any hot pink or purple, red, fuchsia, butter yellow, white or black
Metals: Gold, platinum

Core Colors: Dark or neutralized colors that combine well with your other colors for suits, leathers, pants, sweaters, blouses, dresses, jackets
Pastels: Lightest version of any of your colors to use for stationery, china, linens, housewares, business cards
Coordinating Colors: Colors that work well with your core colors to give richness and life to your wardrobe.
Accent Colors: High vibrant colors, vivid, dramatic, sparkling, they give magnetic flair and fun to either formal or sports clothes

Garnet
RedOrange

Stars: Julia Roberts, Halle Berry, Sigourney Weaver

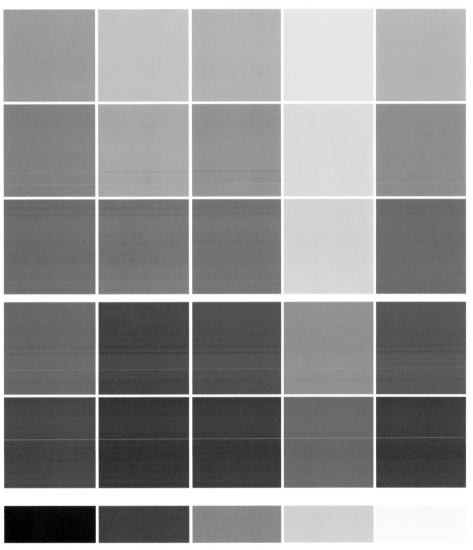

Core: Army tan, chocolate, or bison brown
Neutralized: Dark versions of rust, cinnamon, cloves, moss, or teal
Pastel: Oatmeal, light and medium tans, light versions of any of your colors including red oranges
Amazing Red Orange Color Coordinations: Chocolate with hot orange and goldenrod; beige; teal and rust or bright orange (your version of red, white and blue); moss with goldenrod; antique rose with teal; oatmeal with olive-wood and mistletoe
Accent: Goldenrod, butternut, poppy, any of your hot red orange colors
Metals: Gold, copper, and wood

Core Colors: Dark or neutralized colors that combine well with your other colors for suits, leathers, pants, sweaters, blouses, dresses, jackets
Pastels: Lightest version of any of your colors to use for stationery, china, linens, housewares, business cards
Coordinating Colors: Colors that work well with your core colors to give richness and life to your wardrobe.
Accent Colors: High vibrant colors, vivid, dramatic, sparkling, they give magnetic flair and fun to either formal or sports clothes

Topaz
YellowOrange

Stars: Susan Sarandon

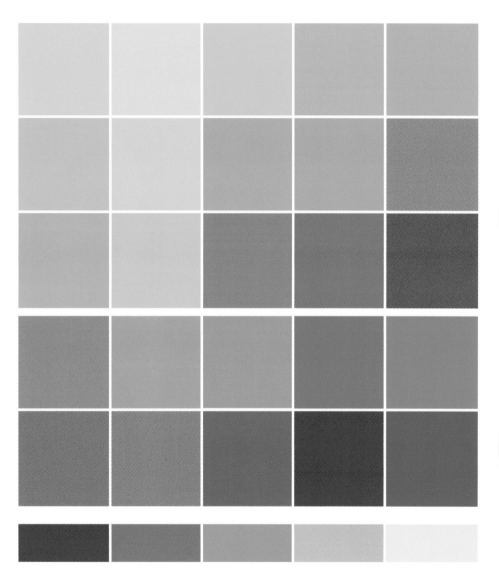

Core: Warm tan, walnut, tobacco, nutmeg

Neutralized: Dusty versions of caramel, ginger, camel, olive, khaki, hemp, clay, mustard

Pastel: light warm tans, ivory, lightest oranges or golds

Stunning Yellow Orange Color Coordinations: walnut with clay and mustard; beige, peacock and pumpkin (your version of red, white and blue); khaki with light peacock or with Aztec gold and citron; salmon with deep peacock

Accent: hot oranges or golds, arabesque, your bright blues, citron

Metals: gold, brass, and wood

Core Colors: Dark or neutralized colors that combine well with your other colors for suits, leathers, pants, sweaters, blouses, dresses, jackets

Pastels: lightest version of any of your colors to use for stationery, china, linens, housewares, business cards

Coordinating Colors: Colors that work well with your core colors to give richness and life to your wardrobe.

Accent Colors: high vibrant colors, vivid, dramatic, sparkling, they give magnetic flair and fun to either formal or sports clothes

Peridot

YellowGreen

Stars: Nicole Kidman

Core: warm tan, spice brown such as nutmeg or light walnut

Neutralized: Dusty versions of banana yellow, jade or willow green, muted tangerine

Pastel: light beige or off white with YG cast, lightest yellows, or lime greens

Intriguing Yellow Green Color Coordinations: sage with willow or banana; spice brown with tangerine and banana; leaf or willow with tiger lily and sea foam; jade with sea blue; melon with deep green and banana, sage with tangerine

Accent: lime green, hot yellow or tiger lily, your red, is exciting with your greens, lavender, sea foam

Metals: gold

Core Colors: Dark or neutralized colors that combine well with your other colors for suits, leathers, pants, sweaters, blouses, dresses, jackets

Pastels: lightest version of any of your colors to use for stationery, china, linens, housewares, business cards

Coordinating Colors: Colors that work well with your core colors to give richness and life to your wardrobe.

Accent Colors: high vibrant colors, vivid, dramatic, sparkling, they give magnetic flair and fun to either formal or sports clothes

Aquamarine
BlueGreen

These examples of color coordinations for the Aquamarine–Blue Green Color Collection show you the many ways you can mix your colors. This is the secret that gives you a closet that works, a closet you can count on to make you look radiant and beautiful–always!

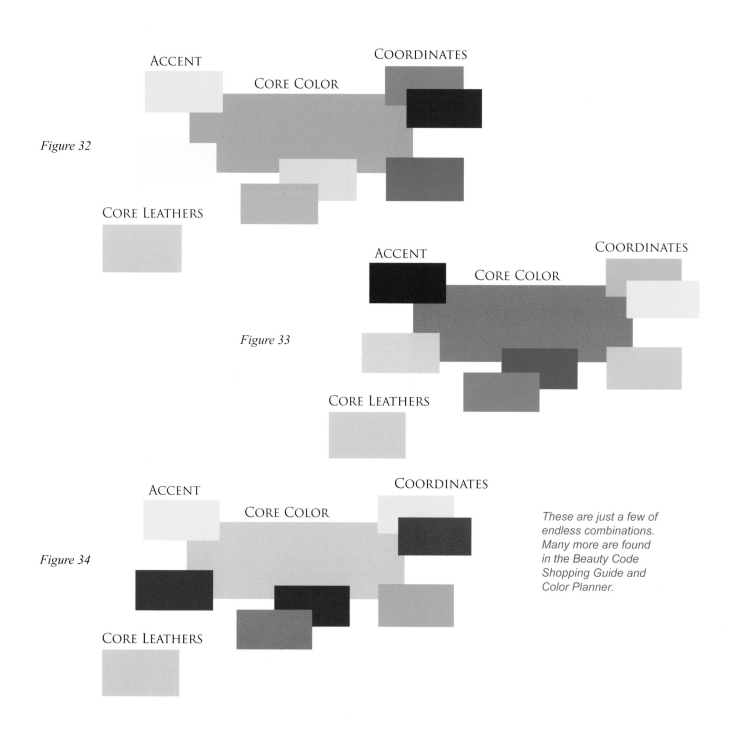

Figure 32

Figure 33

Figure 34

These are just a few of endless combinations. Many more are found in the Beauty Code Shopping Guide and Color Planner.

Sapphire
BluePurple

Examples of Sapphire–Blue Purple color coordinations show you how you can mix colors in unique ways. This secret unlocks closet magic that will easily and immediately give you radiant beauty, as well as inspire you with many stunning and intriguing color combinations.

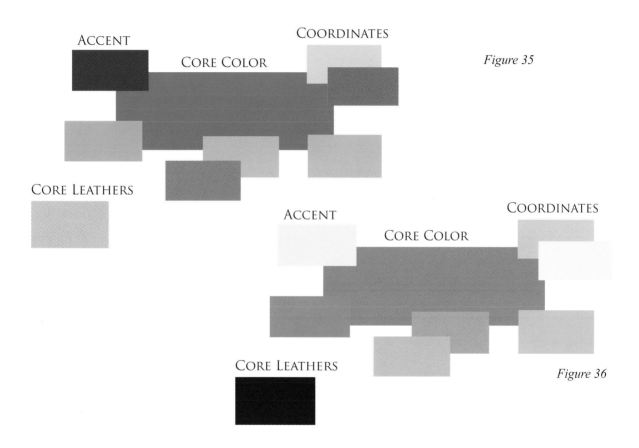

ACCENT

COORDINATES

CORE COLOR

Figure 35

CORE LEATHERS

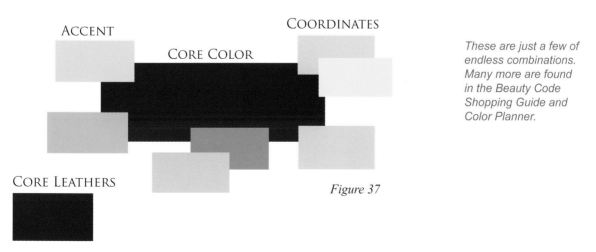

ACCENT

COORDINATES

CORE COLOR

CORE LEATHERS

Figure 36

ACCENT

COORDINATES

CORE COLOR

These are just a few of endless combinations. Many more are found in the Beauty Code Shopping Guide and Color Planner.

CORE LEATHERS

Figure 37

Ruby
RedPurple

The following examples of Ruby–Red Purple color coordinations take you out of the "black & white" rut. Breathtaking rich colors bring out the richness of your skin and dark hair. When you buy your clothes only in these colors, you can count on your closet to reward you with a beautiful appearance for every event.

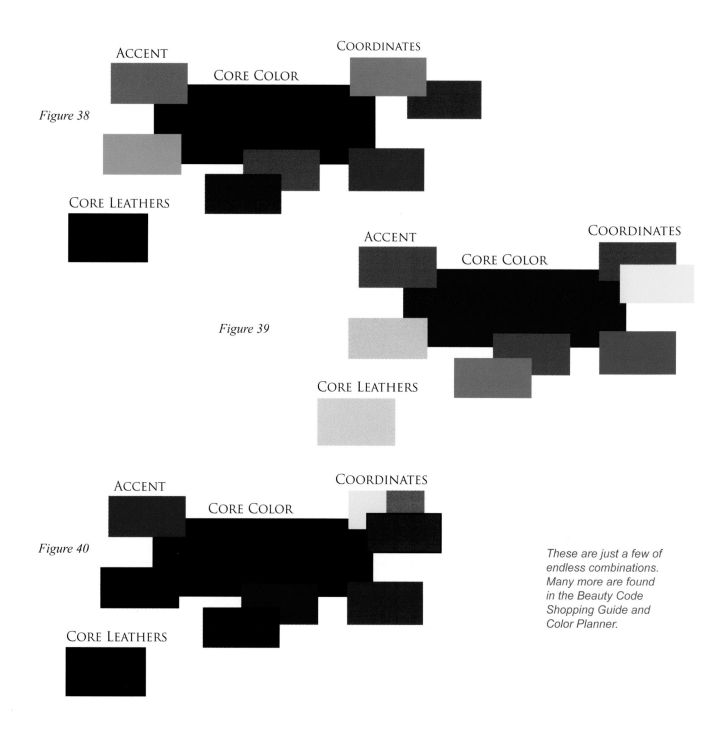

Figure 38

Figure 39

Figure 40

These are just a few of endless combinations. Many more are found in the Beauty Code Shopping Guide and Color Planner.

Garnet
RedOrange

Below you see rich, warm examples of Garnet–Red Orange color coordinations sure to engage and inspire you. Watch your confidence grow in your ability to mix colors. You'll have a closet that you can trust to reward you with quick appearance decisions that make you look good any time, anywhere.

ACCENT CORE COLOR COORDINATES

Figure 41

CORE LEATHERS

ACCENT CORE COLOR COORDINATES

CORE LEATHERS

Figure 42

ACCENT CORE COLOR COORDINATES

CORE LEATHERS

Figure 43

These are just a few of endless combinations. Many more are found in the Beauty Code Shopping Guide and Color Planner.

Topaz
YellowOrange

Your examples of Topaz–Yellow Orange color coordinations give you an amazing number of ways to create exciting outfits. Your color confidence will grow as you learn to work with your colors. You will always look wonderful. It will be easy because everything in your closet will work for you.

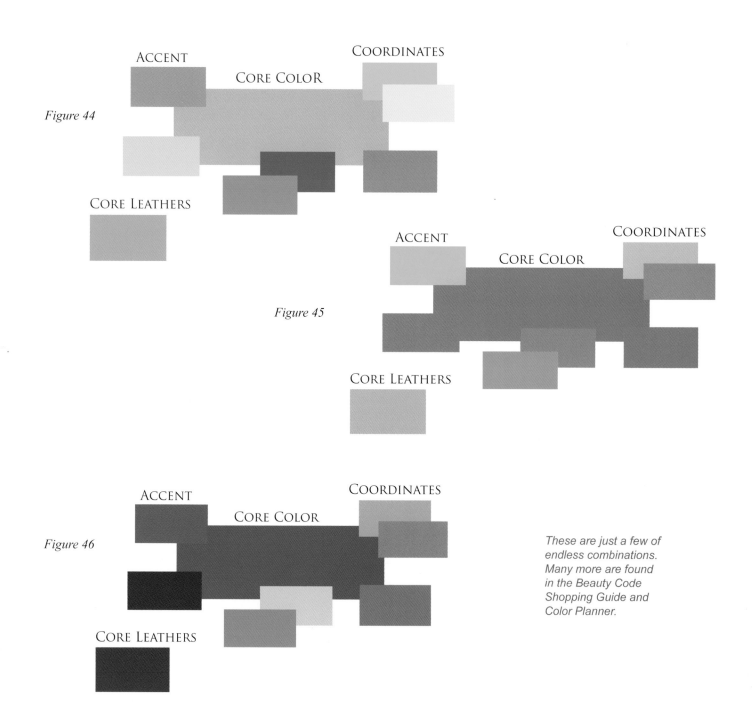

Figure 44

Figure 45

Figure 46

These are just a few of endless combinations. Many more are found in the Beauty Code Shopping Guide and Color Planner.

Peridot
YellowGreen

A special lift and lilt in color is yours when you use these Peridot–Yellow Green color coordinations. Buying your clothes in these colors guarantees that your closet will quickly and easily give you unusual color combinations that make you glow with radiant beauty. You will have confidence and capability in using color.

Figure 47

Figure 48

Figure 49

These are just a few of endless combinations. Many more are found in the Beauty Code Shopping Guide and Color Planner.

COLOR KEY SYSTEM BY ROBERT C. DOOR

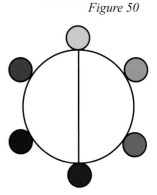

Figure 50

Used by Ameritone Paint, The Color Key System offers two color collections, Color Key One—cool colors and Color Key Two—warm colors. However, there is a challenge with the Color Key System: Using the color wheel in the standard position creates a section of inaccurate color temperatures for people in both Color Key Color Collections. It offers only two color groups, warm and cool, so does not meet the needs created by natural value (light to dark) differences in people: blondes, brownette and brunettes with skin tones light to black. This is an example of incomplete color science.

THE SEASONS

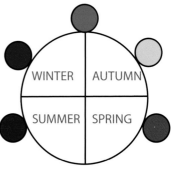

Figure 51

Johan Itten, a German artist, observed that his art students tended to paint landscapes in seasonal color groupings—autumn, winter, summer and spring—consistent with their own coloring. To Suzanne Caygill of San Francisco, this opened the door to the idea of personal coloring based on the seasons. A student of Fashion Academy in Costa Mesa, California, (a company that taught the Seasons concept and tied it to Munsell's Color Wheel), Carol Jackson, took advantage of the wide spread interest in personal color and authored the book, Color Me Beautiful, which turned into a best seller. This color system started out as an observation that became a concept or stratagem to connect people to color. Fashion Academy later tied it to Munsell's Color Wheel. This was the first effort to give people individual colors.

"I've worked with the Beauty Code concept for over 9 years as a designer and find it's the most accurate color concept I've found. I won't buy a toothbrush out of my color group now." —Karen, artist & designer

The Challenge with the Seasons Color System:

The Seasons system uses Munsell's color wheel of five primary colors: red, yellow, green, blue, and purple. Munsell eliminated orange because he felt orange usurped too great a portion of the color wheel. His color wheel is not accurate to light i.e. the colors found in rainbows or prisms. This system does not address 1) accurate color qualities of temperature, hue, value, and intensity for people; 2) laws of complementary and analogous color effects on people; and 3) accurate separation of color qualities for people.

Munsell's color wheel used by the Seasons:

- Temperature is distorted since green is a cool color, red is a warm color.

- Hue is distorted because red is not balanced with an opposite color on the color wheel.

- Value is upside down—the darkest colors are at the top of the color wheel.

- Intensity is not fully met because Summer only offers soft, muted colors and Spring only offers bright colors.

- Autumn includes color undertones from three-fourths of the color wheel.

- Spring and Summer contain color undertones from one half of the color wheel and Winter, with its icicle colors, includes color undertones from the full color wheel.

- Summer, the warmest season, offers the most cool colors.

"Only Marilyn Starr Harris has put her finger on the basis of the principle governed by color law that applies to color typing people. Her revolutionary new color system presents answers that experts world wide have searched for and never found."

—Bob Gervitch, Past Marketing Vice President, Revlon

Warm colors with blended red and yellow undertones are both included in the Autumn collection. Red-based and warm-toned people cannot wear strong yellow undertones so are often placed into a cool collection such as Winter (red undertones) or Summer (blue undertones).

OTHER SYSTEMS:

Other systems have emerged. One claims that we get our coloring from the time of day and offers three color groups: morning, afternoon, and evening. Another breaks the Seasons into months of the year and offers 12 groups of colors. More gimmick concepts or stratagems rather than accurate science.

When we're given the "in" colors for all people by the fashion industry, this is hype. The fashion industry uses this to control colors because it must define color selection to coordinate colors for zippers, thread, buttons, and other.

CONCLUSION:

Enjoy your new color confidence. Create beauty wherever you want beauty to touch your life—and send me pictures of what you create. I'll post them on my website with your name. New fun!

Note: As well as the color information in this chapter, the Beauty Code offers an online Color Discovery. Learn more about that on my website: *wwwyourbeautycode.com*

Personal Beauty Guide

Applying
the Right
Colors
to You

Part II

Makeup is a **good thing** to believe in. Why? When you **know how** to use it, it can **improve** the way you look.

Makeup
the First Place to Start

If you look attractive, you feel attractive and your actions will reflect that. Your self-image affects your influence and opportunities wherever you go. When you see a plain Jane reflected back from your mirror day after day, something negative happens to your self-image. It also affects the mood of your family or associates. More than one husband says his wife's appearance is important in his life. When he leaves a woman who is fresh and beautiful in face, clothing, and attitude, he faces the day with more enthusiasm.

Can you think of an exemplary woman as drab, flat, and unattractive? Not really. Nor can you see her over-painted, garish, and brazen. Between the two is a golden mean: a woman who wants to make the very best of herself because she knows her outer appearance is an expression of the inner woman.

It's very simple to learn and apply skills and timeless principles to look your best every day. We teach you to apply makeup so that the observer sees you—naturally lovely, not just a collection of bright eyeshadow, weird brows, or fad eyelashes.

As in color and line, you need to be knowledgeable about what works for you. When you know what you should do and use, you can't be led amiss.

Makeup should look so natural only you know. It should always present the real you more beautifully. It should never be the main attraction. Therefore, learn how to use it on your individual face. Friend Sue's makeup routine may not work for you.

And doing makeup is not a career. After you learn how, you can apply beautiful makeup in five - ten minutes and professional filming makeup in twenty to thirty minutes.

Some women need very little makeup. Some need quite a bit to define their features. To look terrific, know your needs.

"After getting in the right colors for clothes and makeup, I was getting ready for bed one night and my husband said, 'Do you have to take that off? You look so good.'"
—Judy G.

chapter 7

The purpose of makeup is to smooth the skin, accent the eyes, and subdue any feature that is too-prominent. It isn't meant to cover or hide the skin but rather to enhance its own natural color in perfect blending. It should look so natural for daytime that it isn't noticed. One man stung his wife with the comment that she just wasn't as "naturally beautiful" as another woman. I hurt for his wife; sorry for his thoughtless blindness, yet I was amused. That "naturally beautiful" woman's makeup cabinet is filled to the brim with cosmetics that helped create her lovely face.

Three principle factors create natural makeup: healthy skin, the right colors, applying makeup in the correct shapes, and use the right blending techniques to balance your features. And have the tools you need to get good results.

HEALTHY SKIN

Beautiful, supple, radiant skin is a product of intelligent living. It comes from eating wholesome foods, using proper cleansing methods regularly, getting adequate rest, and exercising regularly. A sluggish digestive tract wrecks havoc with your complexion. So can excessive dieting, worry, hate, fear, fatigue, and lets face it—age.

There are many diet programs that you can choose from to adapt into your life-style. It's up to you to find one that works for you and your body. You can learn about my plan of eating, The Diet of Light and Life, at www.mybeautycode.com.

A basic skin care regime should, at the very least, include these four things: a cleanser, a scrub, a toner, and a moisturizer.

CLEANSER

Find a good cleanser, one formulated for your skin type: oily, combination, or dry. A good cleanser will emulsify hardened oil and soil embedded in your pores so it can be cleansed out and easily washed away, leaving your skin feeling clean and fresh.

SCRUB

A good scrub should give your skin a radiant glow by doing two things: gently exercising your pores to push out any deep soil and gently removing the dead surface skin cells that dull your complexion.

TONER

Toners are specifically formulated to remove the last traces of oil or soil left on your skin and close or tighten your pores. It should leave your skin feeling refreshed.

MOISTURIZER

A good moisturizer nourishes and replenishes moisture in the skin, leaving it rested. An important part of your daily routine, a good moisturizer keeps your skin young, soft, and supple by maintaining its elasticity.

GET READY!

COLLECT THE RIGHT COSMETIC TOOLS

So that you are comfortable and relaxed, to begin, let's use the same terms for cosmetic tools. Here's a list of cosmetic items, in the order of their usual use. In each category, the Beauty Code™ Cosmetic Color Line has exclusive colors based on my Science of Personal Color™. Each of the six Beauty Code™ Cosmetic Collections contains colors specific to that Cosmetic Color Collection.

CONCEALER

Concealer—also called disguise, lid primer, cover-up, and blending crème—is a flesh-toned cream used to hide dark or red areas of the face. A thin film of concealer, placed on the eyelid, keeps eyeshadow in place and the eyeshadow color even and smooth. It comes in a pan, pot, tube, or wand. Other concealer colors besides flesh tones are mint, to cover red; mauve to cover dark spots and ochre (gold) for dark circles on warm toned skins.

FOUNDATION

Foundation, also known as base makeup or makeup base, is a light cream or liquid used on the face to smooth and even out the skin tone and improve the color. Then the other colors you add for eyes, cheeks, and lips are more effective in coloring the face.

Marilyn's foundation is so sheer and feels so natural I don't know I'm wearing it. I love the fact that it never leaves a line at your neck. I've used one color of Marilyn's lipstick for years and it goes with everything I wear.
Monica J.

CONTOUR POWDER

This is a dark powdered eyeshadow used to recess or color areas of the face. Use it to recess a hollow in the cheek, to intensify eyeshadow, as a brow and liner color for the most natural effect. Contour colors are black charcoal through gray, brown, and taupe. Your best brush-on eyebrow color will be your contour color.

I've worked with Marilyn's concept for over nine years as a designer. I always receive compliments on my makeup. I own much less makeup now—but use everything. I love the way I feel about myself.

Karen M.

POWDER

Powder is used on top of makeup to set and give finish to your makeup. A fine powder is usually compressed (pressed powder) in a small compact or loose (loose powder) in a jar.

EYESHADOW

Eyeshadow is a soft powder, made into every color imaginable, to be used on eyelids to create pretty eyes.

HIGHLIGHT EYESHADOW

Highlight eyeshadow is a light powder to use directly under the brows to give the eyebrow distinction from the eyes, or on the eyelids to bring them forward. Highlight colors are white and light beiges, including flesh, muted pink, or soft golden tones.

MASCARA

Mascara is a heavy black (or dark brown, even navy) paste used to darken, thicken, and lengthen lashes.

BLUSH OR ROUGE

Blush or rouge comes in either cream or powder form. It is used to give the cheeks a healthy color, to define a jawline or contour the throat or forehead.

LIP COLOR

This is also called lipstick, gloss, or glosser. It is a creamy paste in tubes, wands, or compacts used to color the lips.

PENCIL LINERS

Pencils, of different styles, are used to line the lips and eyes to give them more definition and distinction.

EYELASH CURLER

Eyelash curlers can be made out of metal or plastic. Use one to curl your lashes and give your eyes a more open, dramatic look.

TWEEZERS

Tweezers may have a pointed tip, slanted tip, or flat tip. Use one to groom your eyebrows for a more inviting look.

EYEBROW BRUSH AND GROOMER

This is a convenient duo brush to groom eyebrows.

APPLYING MAKEUP TO BALANCE YOUR FEATURES

Before applying makeup, you first need to judge and know your features. Your best patterns of makeup application are determined by your structure, regardless of the newest trends. Trends can be adopted to you, but never neglect your own facial structure to follow a trend. Trends change. Structure doesn't. For example, some trends focus on full lips (and women call for a plastic surgeon), or thick lashes (and we go through the contortions of gluing on extra lashes). The "look" can be bright colors, gold sun-burnished colors, or maybe dark, somber colors. No matter the trend, each facial structure requires different and specific needs in color values, intensities, and patterns to balance them.

Barring birth defects or deforming injury, we assume that the faces of most people are the same on both sides - the right half a mirror image of the left half. This is false. Divided down the middle, each half of the face is different, in some people radically different. It's been proposed that one half of your face is maternal (coming from our mother's side) and the other side is paternal (from our father's side). From a makeup artist's view, each side has to be considered independently and makeup applied so both sides look balanced.

"Until you get the right colors you don't realize your beauty. Your colors enhance everything you are. The Beauty Code System enhances the beauty you already had but didn't know how to express. It helps you express yourself fully, outside and inside. It helps you to be more confident because you know how to look your very best and how to do it yourself."

Carol Lee W.,
makeup artist

BRUSHES

1 2 3 4 5 6 7 8 9 10 11 12 13 14

1.   Foundation Brush: Applies an even layer of foundation to skin

2.   Powder Brush: Applies a soft layer of powder to face

3.   Blush Brush: Applies blush or contour powders

4.   Large Angled Fluff Brush: Applies contouring colors to eyelid

5.   Large Oval Flat Brush: Applies even shadow color to eyelid

6.   Large Oval Fluff Brush: Applies a soft layer or dusting of eyeshadow over entire lid

7.   Medium Oval Flat Brush: Applies eyeshadow to lid

8.   Medium Oval Fluff Brush: Applies eyeshadow to lid

9.   Medium Angled Fluff Brush: Applies contouring colors to eyelid

10.   Mini Oval Fluff Brush: Applies eyeshadow to lid

11.   Small Oval Flat Brush: Applies eyeshadow to lid

12.   Small Oval Fluff Brush: Applies eyeshadow to lid

13.   Detail Liner Brush: Applies a precise, clear line to eyes; may be used wet or dry

14.   Angled Flat Brush: Applies a thin or thick line to eyes; may be used wet or dry

TO CHOOSE THE RIGHT COLORS

Your coloring, as you have learned, is unique to you. So your most attractive makeup colors will be those which coordinate with the colors in the Beauty Code™ Color Palette. Simply match your makeup colors to your Color Collection in the book. It's that easy!

With Beauty Code Cosmetics you get your right cosmetic colors.

Cosmetic colors come in basic and fashion colors.

a. Basic Colors: dark to light colors; black or charcoal through grays; brown and taupe; white; light beiges, including flesh, muted pink, or soft golden tones.

b. Fashion Colors: all colors other than the Basic Colors.

Colors can be muted or bright. Muted colors, as opposed to bright colors, are colors that have been grayed down by adding brown or black to them. Bright, advancing colors are made less advancing by mixing them with neutral basic colors (black, brown and gray).

Or you can neutralize, "mute," or tone down a color by mixing it with its complement. To mute green, use pink tones; to mute blue, use an orange tone; to mute purple, use yellow and visa versa. Muted colors have a softer, richer effect than bright colors.

For perfect match cosmetic colors, see the *Beauty Code™ Cosmetic Collections* on pages 146 thru 151. All the matching is done for you, the guesswork is gone.

Here are three quick tips to buying makeup perfect for you:

- Match lipsticks and blush colors to the pinks, corals, oranges, reds, browns, and beiges in your Color Planner; match eyeshadows to any color you want to put on your eyes.

- Choose colors with values (dark to light) close to your natural coloring.

- If you have dark hair or brows, you'll look best in dark, rich, bright, or very light colors. If you are a fair-haired and fair-skinned person, you'll wear pastels, rich, and bright colors best.

The classically proportioned face is divided into five vertical sections. The center section is the space between your eyes. Then the two sections of your eyes themselves are next. Last are the two outside sections from the outer edge of your eyes to the sides of your face. Ideally if all three areas, on both sides of the face, are the same width, the face is balanced.

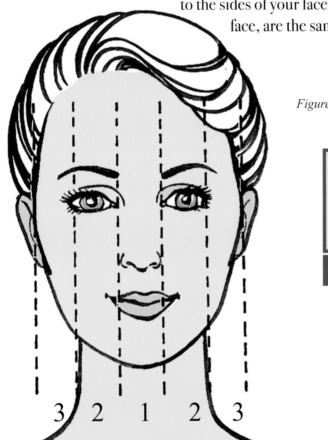

Figure 52

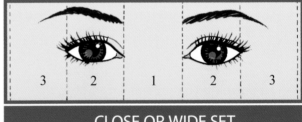

CLOSE OR WIDE SET

If the middle (1) and outside (3) sections are wider than the eyes (2), then the face appears to have small eyes that are wide-set.

If the middle (1) section is more narrow than (2), the eyes appear to be close-set.

If space (3) between the outer edge of your eye and hairline is narrow, move the hair outward showing the edge of face. Keep your eyeshadow pattern close to the outside edge of the eye.

If space (3) between the outer edge of your eye and hairline is wide, bring the hair forward onto sides of the face. Extend the shadow pattern beyond the outside edge of the eye.

Regarding mouth width, ideally, the corners of the mouth should line up directly beneath the pupils of the eye.

Fill in the Face and Features Summary Worksheets on pages 129, 130, and 131.

NOSES

Figure 53

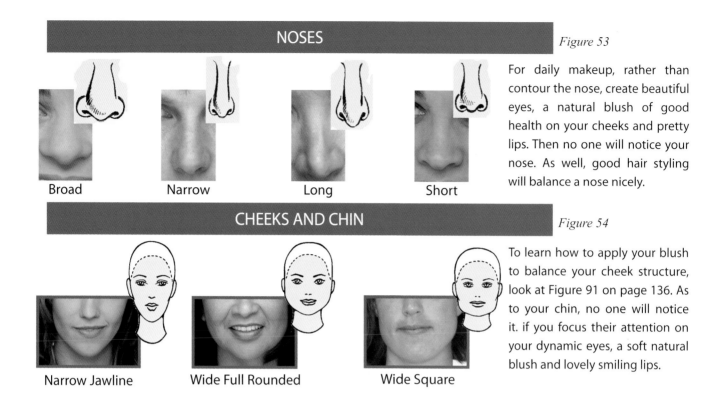

Broad   Narrow   Long   Short

For daily makeup, rather than contour the nose, create beautiful eyes, a natural blush of good health on your cheeks and pretty lips. Then no one will notice your nose. As well, good hair styling will balance a nose nicely.

CHEEKS AND CHIN

Figure 54

Narrow Jawline   Wide Full Rounded   Wide Square

To learn how to apply your blush to balance your cheek structure, look at Figure 91 on page 136. As to your chin, no one will notice it. if you focus their attention on your dynamic eyes, a soft natural blush and lovely smiling lips.

THE PARTS OF THE EYE

Now that you understand your face better, let's focus on your eyes and eyebrows. Take the time to become skillful in creating graceful eyebrow and eyeshadow shapes. Eyes communicate. A weird brow shape or an eyeshadow that is too-vivid will easily distract anyone during a during a conversation.

Figure 55

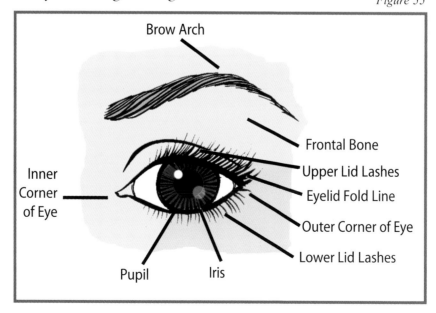

Brow Arch

Inner Corner of Eye

Frontal Bone
Upper Lid Lashes
Eyelid Fold Line
Outer Corner of Eye
Lower Lid Lashes

Pupil   Iris

Figure 56

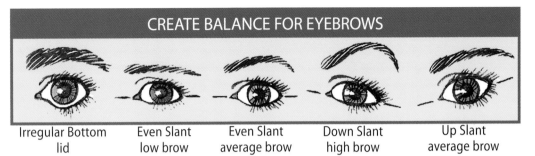

CREATE BALANCE FOR EYEBROWS

| Irregular Bottom lid | Even Slant low brow | Even Slant average brow | Down Slant high brow | Up Slant average brow |

— see living examples on pages 132-134

Eyebrows help frame and emphasize your eyes. Once you take the time to create a beautiful eyebrow shape, grooming and coloring your eyebrows will be simple. Use a small, stiff eyeshadow brush, apply a natural shadow color that matches your hair color to your eyebrows. Follow the natural shape of your eyebrow.

STEP ONE

First, brush your brows straight up toward your hairline. This frees the hairs from makeup and tangles. Then, with a single sweep, move your spiral brush along the top edge of the brow from the inner to the outer edge to finish the shape.

As a general rule, shape brows by following the natural line of the brow.

Figure 57

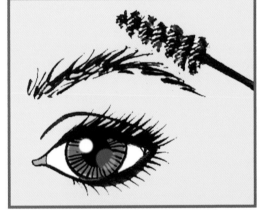

Brush your brows straight up toward your hairline.

Brush along the top edge of the brow, from inner to outer.

Figure 58

NATURAL SHAPES FOR BROWS

Too achieve a natural-looking brow use even lines and balance the brow thickness to the face.

Figure 59

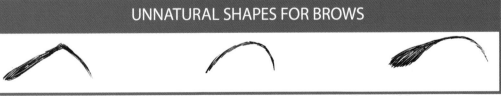

UNNATURAL SHAPES FOR BROWS

Unnatural brow-shapes have sharp angles, sharp arched curves, uniform widths, or exaggerated different widths.

If some eyebrow hairs are too long, brush all hairs straight *up* using the spiral brush, then cut the extra long hairs to conform with the curved upper edge of the brow. *Always* leave 1/4 inch between the top of the brow and where you cut. Don't cut them too closely or they'll look stubby.

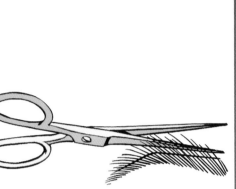

Figure 60

STEP TWO

1. First, get the right brow color. Here is a quick and easy way to determine a natural color for your brows that will match and enhance your natural coloring. Simply find your hair color in the left column, and see the corresponding brow color in the right column. In most cases, I prefer brown powder applied with a brow brush.

HAIR COLOR	RECOMMENDED BROW COLOR
Dark, Brunette	Black or Charcoal, a 2B pencil is also good
Brownettes	Kohl Brown or Charcoal
Blondes	Light or Medium Brown, Taupe
Red	Walnut
Warm Gray	Light Brown
Cool Gray	Taupe

2. Next, shape the brow. Contrary to intuition, in eyebrow shaping, the bottom of the brow is more important than the top. Get the bottom right and the top will be easy.

So, choose your best natural brow color and follow the steps on the next page to do your brows.

Figure 61

a.   b.   c.   d.   e.

a. Draw the beginning bottom line of the brow with an eyebrow pencil or a brush, using short, fine strokes.
b. Draw the bottom line up to the arch.
c. Draw the underside of the arch. The outside end of the brow should be slightly higher than its beginning to give a feeling of lifting.
d. Draw the top line parallel to the bottom brow line up and over the arch. Complete the top line by connecting it to the end of the bottom brow line.
e. Brush your brow hair up and across the newly drawn top line of brow. Fill in the rest of the brow if necessary. This method gives a well defined but soft brow line.

Figure 62

NATURAL STARTING SHAPES

The thick inside portion of the eyebrow can take a number of natural shapes. The best shape for your face depends on the structure of your face.

Figure 63

If you have close set eyes, give the impression of greater width between them by beginning the brow slightly back of the eye's inner corner and apply most of your eyeshadow toward the outside of the eye.

Eyeshadow patterns for close set eyes are on page 133.

BROWS FOR CLOSE SET EYES

STEP THREE

Tweeze away any hairs outside the drawn brows, and between the brows.

Light eyebrow hairs are hard to see and thus difficult to tweeze, but any hairs between the brow and the eye will hold extra eyeshadow and create a muddy shadow pattern. Waxing is sometimes a better way of removing light, fine hair. Once you are happy with your shaped brow, set aside time each week to simply maintain and upkeep your shape, plucking when necessary.

If you have a straight brow, give it shape by plucking out extra brow hairs, either on the top ends or the center bottom with a slight arch, or both. After shaping the brows, again brush them with your brow brush to give them a smooth, natural look. If you need color in your brows, add brush on brow color or brow pencil now.

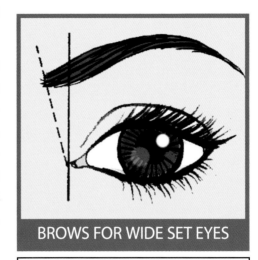

BROWS FOR WIDE SET EYES

Figure 64: If you have wide-set eyes, give the impression of balance by beginning the brow slightly before the eye's inner corner. Apply eyeshadow closer to the center above your eye. Eyeshadow patterns for wide-set eyes are found on page 133.

Figure 64

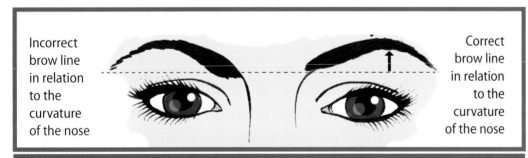

Incorrect brow line in relation to the curvature of the nose

Correct brow line in relation to the curvature of the nose

Figure 65

CORRECT BEGINNING BROW LINES

Because the line of the nose curves naturally from the bone above the eye socket, it's best to give a straight edge to the bottom inner edge of the brow rather than one that follows the downward curve shown in figure 65. The natural brow line will indicate where the brow should peak, or reach its highest point. Natural brows arch anywhere within the arrows shown. The top line of the brow peak should be slightly in front or in back of the bottom peak rather than peaking right together so the brow doesn't look like a teepee.

Now that your eyes are framed with beautiful brows, it's time to apply makeup. This can take five to twenty minutes depending on you and the effect you want for the event your attending. Be sure to start with a clean, fresh palette (your face) for the best makeup application.

Here are the basic steps for natural makeup application.

    a. Apply concealer and foundation to smooth your skin

    b. Groom and color brows

    c. Apply basic eyeshadow, then add fashion eyeshadows

    d. Apply mascara

    e. Apply blush

    f. Apply lipstick or lip gloss

CONCEALER AND FOUNDATION

Concealer, also known as lid primer, cover-up, or blending cream, can be used to hide dark circles, red areas, or scars on the face. It comes in flesh tone, mint (to cover red), mauve (to cover dark spots), and ochre (a gold color to cover dark circles on warm skin tones). Apply a thin layer over eyelids and on problem areas for a quick fix. Include the inner corners of the eye, the entire eyelid up to the brow and directly on any blemishes. You can apply a thin line down the middle of a short nose to make it appear longer.

"I was happy to know I didn't need to wear more makeup, but just apply the right colors in the right areas and ways to enhance my appearance. After being very confused with the Season's system, I finally understand how color plays a major part in how we look and feel."

—*Janet Seamons*
Utah State Contest Winner
Mrs. Senior America
Mother/Daughter Look Alike
with daughter, Brooke

After concealer, apply a foundation to your forehead, nose, cheeks, and over your mouth. Blend it lightly on the edges of the your face and neck. Do not apply it to your eyelids. This light cream or liquid will smooth and even out your skin tone and improve your overall color.

One common mistake women make with their makeup is to run makeup colors or patterns together. For a pleasing appearance, each feature must have clean space around it.

Figure 66 shows the "question mark" approach that gives light or clean space around each feature. This gives each feature its own distinction.

First, keep light space (A) beneath the brows so that eyeshadow does not blur into the brow color.

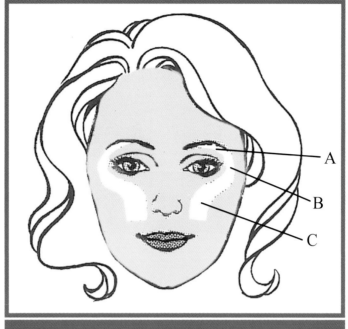

A MORE NATURAL MAKEUP PATTERN

Second, maintain light space (B) between the eyes and cheek, so that cheek color doesn't blur into the eye makeup.

Third, keep light space (C) between the nose and the blush color to separate the nose and cheek areas.

NOTES: Correct makeup colors will go well with all your clothes, so there is no need to get makeup to match every outfit. You no longer waste money on makeup that just sits in your drawer. You now know how to buy colors for yourself that will look good on you, today, tomorrow, and forever.

As fashion trends come and go, beauty consultants often rule out specific uses of makeup or clothing. For example, sometimes eye or lip liners are "in," or sometimes they're "out" of style. I've learned that what is "in" is what the client needs. If you have a ragged lip line, you need lip liner to define and shape your lips. If you don't happen to be a dark-eyed beauty, eyeliner will bring the distinctness of your eyes up quite a few notches.

When I direct photography on men, I often use eyeliner to make their eyes more distinct. So don't be intimidated by what fashion dictates is "in" or "out." You want to look current but have the good sense to know how to use the tools you need to look fabulous in any fashion era.

EYESHADOW

With eyeshadow you can create soft, dewy eyes, or dark, dramatic eyes. You can make small eyes look larger and large eyes smaller to balance the face. Make your eye color deep, rich and inviting because the eyes are the main feature of your face.

Bare Eye

Simple Eye Pattern

Deep, Intense and Accented Pattern

Figure 67

The basic process of applying eyeshadow is to first shape your eye with the Simple Eyeshadow Contour and Highlight Pattern using Basic Colors. Then deepen, intensify, and accent your eyes with Fashion Colors.

The chart below outlines the Basic Colors to use according to your hair color, and/or the results of your color quiz. These colors are based on the color combinations in your color group.

HAIR COLOR	BASIC CONTOUR COLORS
Brunettes	Charcoal or Black Pearl
Brownettes	
Blue Purple	Cool Brown, Night Dove
Red or Yellow Orange	Warm Brown, Russian Sable
Blondes	
Blue Green	Light Cool Brown, Fawn Mist
Yellow Green	Light Warm Brown, Warm Spice
Redheads	Walnut
Warm Gray	Light Brown or Walnut
Cool Gray	Taupe

Figure 68

SIMPLE EYESHADOW CONTOUR AND HIGHLIGHT PATTERNS

The following instructions will help you shape and enhance your eye with contour and highlight. Because different eye shapes exist, different eyeshadow patterns are required. They are illustrated at the end of this section. I teach classic analysis and application, rather than trend. Once you learn the classics you can adapt trends where and when you want to follow them.

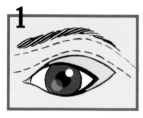

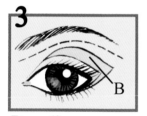

Figure 69

The Simple Eyeshadow Pattern is:

1. Place highlight eyeshadow just beneath the brow about the width of the shadow brush or sponge. This separates the brow from the shadow pattern with light space.

2. Place darker contour shadow on the eyelid, matching the depth or darkness of the eyeshadow to the depth of your hair and/or brows. Make the darkest area above the iris and blend to each corner of the eye. See A.

3. With a medium shadow, fill in between the top line of the dark contour shadow pattern parallel to, but separated from, the bottom line of the highlight shadow pattern. See B. This will help you determine the correct shape for the shadow on your frontal bone.

There is no great mystery to eyeshadow shapes because they are based on structure, and structure doesn't change until about age forty-five when the skin starts to droop. After that time, keep your eyebrow and shadow patterns moving up on the outside edges; use lighter eyeshadow tones.

To determine how far to extend the shadow pattern out on the side, look for the natural contour line of the frontal bone, which will guide you in selecting the correct eyeshadow pattern. See figures 55 and 70.

DEEPEN, INTENSIFY AND ACCENT

Once you have shaped your eye with contour and highlight, you're ready to intensify and coordinate your eyeshadow with Fashion Colors. To create memorable, deep, beautiful eyes, intensify with dark liners and darker shadows at the outer edge of the eyes.

To intensify and add depth to our eyes, lift the upper eyelid and apply dark liner pencil right beneath the lashes. Eyeliner creates a look of full, thick lashes. Put just the tip of your shadow sponge into dark brown powder and apply a soft smudge for a softer, more natural look that a clearly drawn line right under your bottom lashes and/or along the root edge of the top lashes. You can use pencil or liquid as well, but stipple it to soften the effect.

EYE AREAS TO INTENSIFY

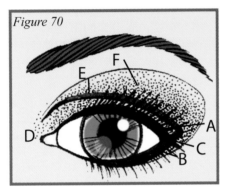

Figure 70

A. Along the edge of the upper lashes

B. Along the edge of the lower outer lashes

C. Along the outer corner of the eye

D. Along the inner corner of the eye

E. Above the iris

F. In the crease between the frontal bone and lid

Figure 71

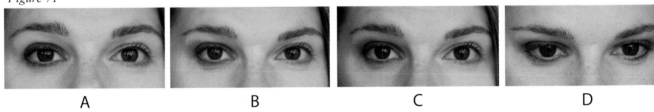

A   B   C   D

Eye makeup was applied only to the eye on the left (on the page) in A, B and C, but to both eyes in D. The "bare" eye is on the right.

  A. To intensify and give the feeling of full, thick lashes, we added pencil eyeliner to the upper and lower lid as well as the outside corner of the eye, then we smudged it with shadow powder.

  B. Next we added contour eyeshadow to the outside and inside of the lid and frontal bone gives curve and depth to the eye. Compare the curve and depth of the finished eye to the "bare" eye on the right.

  C. Now we added fashion colors in small amounts *over* the basic contour pattern to finish the shadows. Then we applied mascara.

  D. Eyes deepened, intensified, and toned to our model's right colors.

FACE AND FEATURES SUMMARY WORKSHEET

Feature   Feature Description

FOREHEAD

1. High	A. High	B. Average	C. Low
2. Avg.	A. High	B. Average	C. Low
3. Low	A. High	B. Average	C. Low

BROWS

1. Height	A. High	B. Average	
2. Density	A. Thick	B. Average	
3. Shape	A. Straight	B. Average	C. Tepee D. High Curve

EYES

1. Slant	A. Up	B. Even
2. Size	A. Small	B. Average
3. Width	A. Close-set	B. Equal
4. Outer edge	A. Narrow	B. Equal
5. Set	A. Deep-set	B. Average

NOSES

1. Width	A. Broad	B. Average	C. Narrow
2. Size	A. Small	B. Average	C. Large
3. Shape	A. Irregular	B. Average	C. Attractive
4. Length	A. Short	B. Average	C. Long

CHEEKS

1. Contour	A. Flat	B. Average	C. Contoured D. Full

CHIN

1. Shape	A. Pointed	B. Average	C. Square D. Round
2. Jaw Set	A. Even	B. Average	C. Wide

LIPS

1. Fullness	A. Thin	B. Average	C. Full
2. Width	A. Narrow	B. Average	C. Wide
3. Line	A. Straight	B. Corners down	C. Pretty Line
4. Size	A. Small	B. Average	C. Large
5. Teeth	A. Attractive	B. Average	C. Crooked

To analyze your face objectively, draw an outline of your face, neck and shoulders on a large mirror using the point of a small bar of soap. Stand about 12 inches from your mirror.

Mark: 1. The top of your head.

2. The top of your hairline, then draw the entire outline of your face, neck and shoulders.

3. Draw the shape of your brows, eyes, nose and mouth, then measure your face as shown in Figures 73 and 74.

4. Measure your face from the top of your head to your chin. Divide this head length measurement in half. This is your ideal balance.

Draw in top of head, hairline, shape of brows, eyes, nose, and mouth. Your outline will look similar to this.

Figure 72

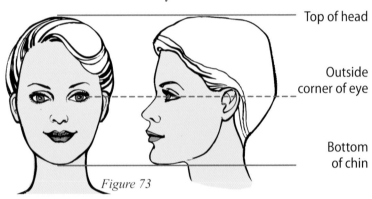

Top of head

Outside corner of eye

Bottom of chin

Figure 73

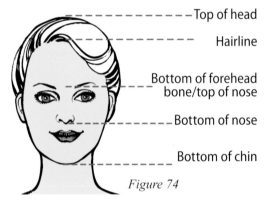

Top of head

Hairline

Bottom of forehead bone/top of nose

Bottom of nose

Bottom of chin

Figure 74

To get your actual balance, measure from the top of your head to your eye and from the eye to the chin. Compare your actual measurement to the ideal measurement.

TOP OF HEAD TO EYE:

Short: Add height to hair style. Wear hair off forehead.

Long: Use hair styles that are flatter on top, wear bangs, apply blush to the top of your forehead.

EYE TO CHIN:

Short: Put blush more on the outside edge of your cheeks and higher on the sides

Long: Bring blush more to the center of your cheeks. Wear lip color in straighter patterns and brighter colors.

Measure from the front hairline to your chin. Divide your face length in thirds. These are the ideal proportions of your face. To get your face proportions compare your actual measurements to the ideal proportions.

Match the outline of your face in Figure 72 with the face outline options you see in Figure 74.

FOREHEAD:

Short: Wear hair off your forehead

Long: Wear bangs, apply blush at the top of your forehead

NOSE:

Short: Put a thin line of highlight down the center of your nose. Put blush more on the outside edge of your cheeks and higher on the sides.

Long: Bring blush more to the center of your cheeks. Wear lip color in straighter patterns.

JAW/CHIN:

Short: Use blush on the outside edge of your neck.

Long: Wear stronger lip colors, use hairstyles that cut that length or move attention elsewhere with earrings, necklaces, or clothing neckline effects.

Next analyze your features according to the options pages 129-138. Circle those. To know your best makeup patterns, match your features to the instructions given in this chapter.

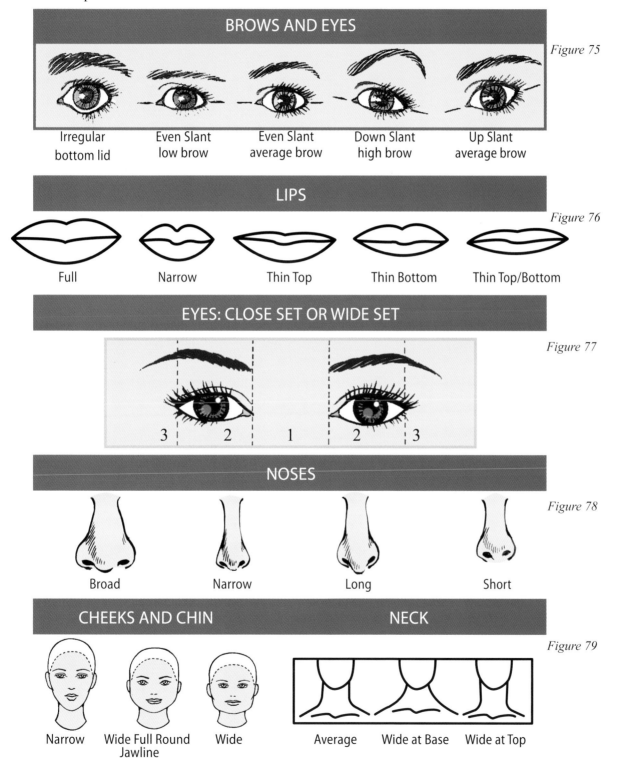

BROWS AND EYES

Figure 75

Irregular bottom lid | Even Slant low brow | Even Slant average brow | Down Slant high brow | Up Slant average brow

LIPS

Figure 76

Full | Narrow | Thin Top | Thin Bottom | Thin Top/Bottom

EYES: CLOSE SET OR WIDE SET

Figure 77

3 | 2 | 1 | 2 | 3

NOSES

Figure 78

Broad | Narrow | Long | Short

CHEEKS AND CHIN   **NECK**

Figure 79

Narrow | Wide Full Round Jawline | Wide   Average | Wide at Base | Wide at Top

EYESHADOW PATTERNS FOR DIFFERENT EYE SHAPES

As I mentioned earlier, different eye shapes require different eyeshadow patterns to shape the eye. For your assistance, the shapes in these drawings are drawn with distinct lines and the shadow patterns are coded. After you place your eyeshadows in patterns, blend them into the soft muted shadows that create beautiful eyes. Assess your eyes using the left side, then use the pattern on the right to balance and create. Once you know your eye shape, you can follow the directions that follow to intensity your look.

●●● Eyeliner

▨ Medium Eyeshadows

▨ Darkest Eyeshadows

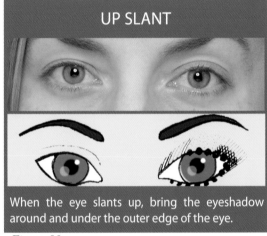

UP SLANT

When the eye slants up, bring the eyeshadow around and under the outer edge of the eye.

Figure 80

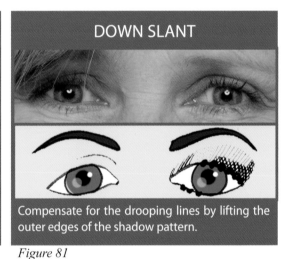

DOWN SLANT

Compensate for the drooping lines by lifting the outer edges of the shadow pattern.

Figure 81

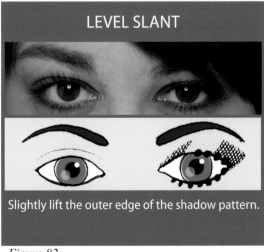

LEVEL SLANT

Slightly lift the outer edge of the shadow pattern.

Figure 82

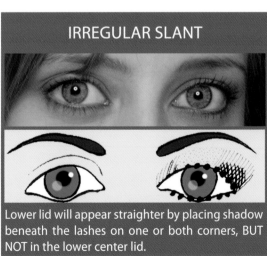

IRREGULAR SLANT

Lower lid will appear straighter by placing shadow beneath the lashes on one or both corners, BUT NOT in the lower center lid.

Figure 83

PROMINENT

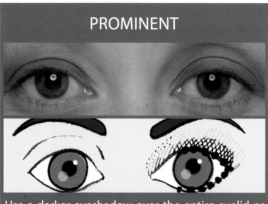

Use a darker eyeshadow over the entire eyelid or only on the ball of the eyelid with medium color on corners of eye.

Figure 84

DEEP SET

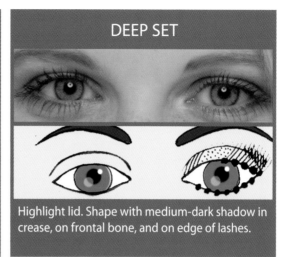

Highlight lid. Shape with medium-dark shadow in crease, on frontal bone, and on edge of lashes.

Figure 85

FULL UPPER LID

Apply medium-dark shadow on outer and inner third of the lid with lighter shadow in center.

Figure 86

FLAT, HOODED

Use dark shadow in a curved line where a natural lid crease would be and on the corners of the eye, with lighter color in center.

Figure 87

CLOSE SET

Start shadow about a third of the way back from the inner corner of the eye and extend it about the same distance beyond the outer corner.

Figure 88

WIDE SET

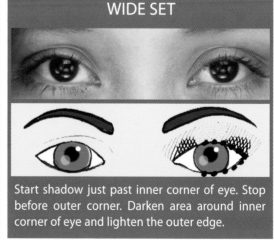

Start shadow just past inner corner of eye. Stop before outer corner. Darken area around inner corner of eye and lighten the outer edge.

Figure 89

LOW BROW

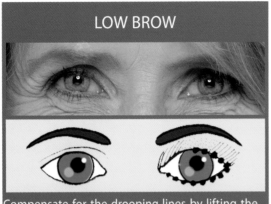

Compensate for the drooping lines by lifting the outer edges of the shadow pattern.

Figure 90

HIGH BROW

Compensate for the drooping lines by lifting the outer edges of the shadow pattern.

Figure 91

SMALL

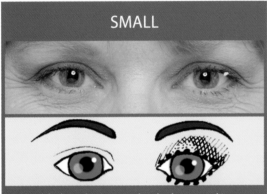

Use highlight color just under the brow and in center of lid. Contour the lid crease and outside edge of eye with darker color and liner.

Figure 92

LARGE

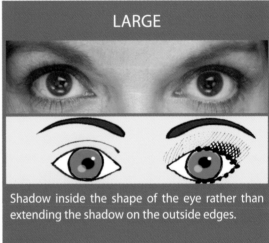

Shadow inside the shape of the eye rather than extending the shadow on the outside edges.

Figure 93

ROUND

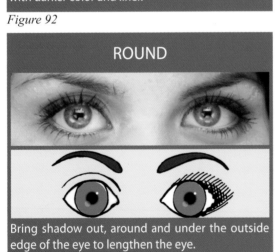

Bring shadow out, around and under the outside edge of the eye to lengthen the eye.

Figure 94

LONG/NARROW

Use rounding eyeshadow shapes and apply white pencil or concealer in the deep creases. Avoid dark shadows in creases.

Figure 95

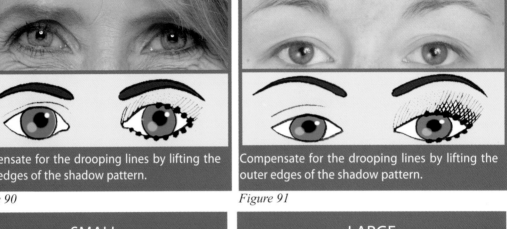

DARK CIRCLES/PUFFY

Apply concealer in creases and over dark areas. Blend gently. Apply foundation over top.

Figure 96

AGED/WRINKLED/CREASED

Use softer, muted eyeshadows in lifting patterns as you would for a Down Slant Eye.

Figure 97

MASCARA

Apply mascara for the final touch. Fill the wand with mascara, then move the loaded wand from the base of the lashes out to their end, rotating the wand as you go. At the same time, move the wand from side to side to coat the side of the lashes.

Do not apply mascara to straight lashes or to lashes on the bottom edge of a down-slanting eye. The increased darkness will intensify the straight lashes or downward slant.

Keeping a Steady Hand

Here's a simple artist's trick to give you firm, even makeup strokes. Place your ring and little finger on your face to stabilize your hand. This lets you apply the makeup firmly and deftly. Hold your tools like a pencil.

BLUSH

Leave a clean space to separate the blush area from the nose, eyes, mouth, and jawline. Two or three cheek colors often appear more natural than just one. The best blush colors are those matching the pink, coral, orange, or brown tones from your Color Collection.

Figure 98

To use a three cheek color system, first use a brown liner pencil or dark dusty blush to contour in the hollow of your cheeks, as shown with the dotted lines in the figure to the right. Then use medium intensity blush to create the blush pattern on cheeks. Use light or bright blush color on the top of the cheekbone and/or the apple of the cheek to highlight the blush (x). This will give the rest of the pattern more depth. Do not apply blush closer to the nose than the middle of the eye nor below the hollow of the cheek.

As with eyeshadow, blush can balance portions of the face giving the impression of that classical symmetry and balance that is the Western ideal of beauty. For example, blush along the edge of the jaw can give it more definition and a look of strength (o). Add blush to the temples to make the forehead more prominent and to add warmth to the eyes. Blush around the hairline adds a healthy glow to the face and makes the forehead appear lower. A touch of blush added to the tip of the nose will make it seem a little shorter, while blush on the chin helps shorten the face. Rouge on the earlobes or on the white creases of the neck or throat helps to create a warm glow and blend the colors of the neck and face. Full cheeks are slimmed by diagonal blush patterns in muted tones.

A. Wide, full, round cheeks

B. To add youthfulness to appearance

C. Thin jaw, full cheek

D. Thin angular cheeks

Figure 99

LIPSTICK OR LIP GLOSS

Lip color defines the mouth and highlights your smile. It can take attention away from such unattractive features as a crooked nose or a double chin.

Apply lip liner by following the natural shape of your lips or follow the instructions for lip shapes that need adjusting. Soften the line by blotting it with a tissue or stippling it gently with your fingertips. Apply two shades of lipstick, one for the main color and a second lighter one on the inner part of the lips to advance and contour them.

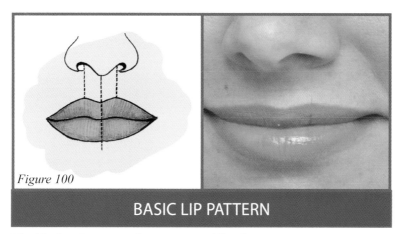

Figure 100

BASIC LIP PATTERN

Ideal balancing, mouth to nose and lip shape.

LIP COLOR ON DIFFERENT SHAPES

If your lips are slightly uneven, then here are some quick tips to balance your lips to make them appear more full or thin.

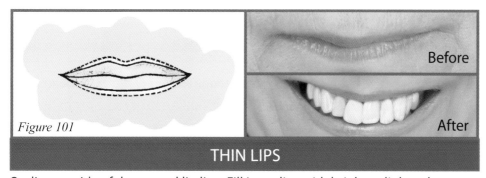

Figure 101

Before

After

THIN LIPS

Outline outside of the natural lip line. Fill inner lips with bright or light color.

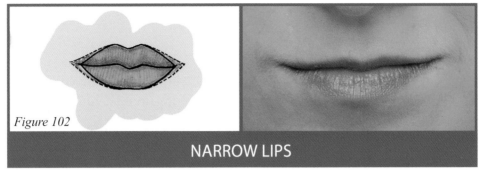

Figure 102

NARROW LIPS

Extend lips by drawing longer edges with lip liner and fill in with brighter color.

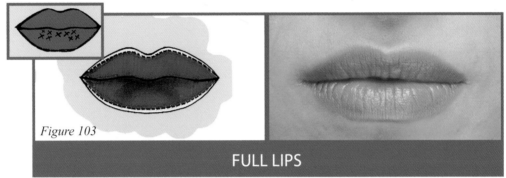

Figure 103

FULL LIPS

Apply dark liner to outline the lips. Blend lipstick over liner, then apply brighter lipstick on the inner part of lips.

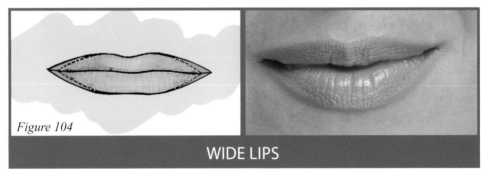

Figure 104

WIDE LIPS

First apply white concealer to the outer edge, cover with makeup. Then, draw an outline on inside width of your lip line.

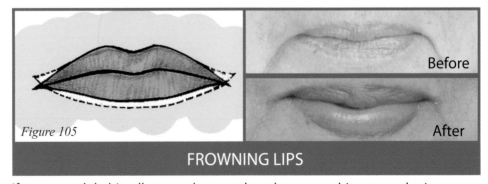

Before

After

Figure 105

FROWNING LIPS

If your mouth habitually turns down at the edges, use white concealer in corners and around your lip edge. Cover with makeup. Outline slightly outside natural lip line, move corners up. Apply a medium shade of lipstick over that drawn line.

THREE SPEED MAKEUP ROUTINES

I was serious when I said these simple makeup techniques could work for you in from five to twenty minutes a day. Here are three makeup routines of different speeds and levels of complexity. Choose the one that fits into your lifestyle and need.

QUICK FIVE MINUTE MAKEUP

1. Clean skin and apply moisturizer
2. Apply concealer to eyelids and blemishes
3. Apply foundation
4. Groom and color brows
5. Apply basic eyeshadow, then add fashion eyeshadows
6. Apply mascara
7. Apply blush
8. Put on lipstick

STANDARD TEN MINUTE MAKEUP

1. Clean skin and apply moisturizer
2. Apply concealer to eyelids and blemishes
3. Apply foundation
4. Apply powder
5. Groom and color brows
6. Apply and blend eyeliner
7. Apply highlight and basic eyeshadow pattern, then add fashion eyeshadows
8. Apply contour and highlight blush colors
9. Apply two lip colors (one to color, one to contour)
10. Finish with mascara

PROFESSIONAL MAKEUP IN THIRTY MINUTES PLUS

1. Clean skin and apply moisturizer

2. Groom brows

3. Contour face with both white and dark contour cream (see below)

4. Cover eyelids and blemishes with concealer

5. Apply makeup foundation

6. Apply cream blush

7. Apply powder

8. Re-groom and color brows

9. Apply and blend eyeliner

10. Apply three or more eyeshadows: highlight, basic, and fashion colors

11. Apply contour and highlight cheek colors to cheeks, jaw, and neck

12. Apply two lipsticks and a gloss cover

13. Apply mascara

14. Gently add a touch of light moisturizer beneath eyes for dewy look

APPLYING HIGHLIGHT AND CONTOUR SHADOWS

1. 2. 3. 4.

Figure 106

1. Areas to Highlight (white or mint colored). In corners of and under eyes. Areas on the face you wish to bring forward: top of cheekbones, nose, frontal bones.

2. Cover Highlight with Concealer (flesh colored).

3. Areas to Contour with dark or medium contour (eyeshadow) powder. Areas on the face you wish to recess or areas on the edge of the face you wish to outline: jawline, chin, hollow of cheek. *Never apply color to double chin.*

4. Blush patterned and blended on the face gives a healthy glow over the entire face.

Makeup
should
serve you, not *stress* you.
The right colors alone
work MAGIC on your face.

GROOMING QUIZ

Learning to be lovely is a matter of knowledge and practice. Rate yourself according to the score below and if you aren't satisfied with your score, don't scold yourself. Simply choose one or two areas to improve. If your score is below 150, it's too low, but you can work on your "sometimes" and "no" areas and improve.

YES–5   SOMETIMES–3   NO–1

1. Do you spend fifteen to thirty minutes first thing in the morning on daily grooming?
2. Do you bathe or shower daily?
3. Do you occasionally take a nurturing bubble or moisturizing oil bath?
4. Do you clean your face, ears, and neck morning and night?
5. Do you use cologne, perfume, or lotion daily?
6. Do you use deodorant daily, twice if needed?
7. Do you remove leg and underarm hair weekly?
8. Do you wear fresh lingerie and hosiery each day?
9. Do you brush your teeth twice a day?
10. Do you use dental floss or picks to clean and stimulate your teeth?
11. Do you keep your breath sweet with mouthwash or mints?
12. Do you see your dentist at least once a year?
13. Do you vary your hairstyle occasionally?
14. Do you use conditioners regularly to keep your hair healthy?
15. Do you keep clean brushes and combs?
16. Do you brush your hair daily? Massage your scalp?
17. Do you shampoo your hair at least twice a week?
18. Do you keep your hands soft with lotion?
19. Are your nails filed smooth at a becoming length?
20. Do you scrub under and around your fingernails, push your cuticle back and apply moisturizer?
21. Is your nail polish smooth, free from chips, and in appropriate colors?
22. While doing heavy work do you protect your hands with gloves?
23. Do you keep an emery board in your purse to repair nail tears?
24. Do you trim your toenails weekly?
25. Do you use a foot deodorant or powder for perspiring feet?

26. Do you properly wrap and dispose of sanitary napkins/ tampons?

27. Do you blend your makeup carefully, especially on the jawline?

28. Do you fix your hair and apply makeup everyday as you would for special events?

29. Do you use moisturizer daily to keep your face and neck young?

30. Do you avoid squeezing pimples and blackheads?

31. Do you keep your hands away from your face?

32. Do you keep your facial expressions pleasant?

33. Do you keep pins in your purse for an emergency clothing repair, then mend your clothes promptly?

34. Are your hems even and straight?

35. Do you promptly replace all missing buttons, snaps, and hooks?

36. Are your shoes in good repair, firm, and well-polished?

37. Are your clothes well-pressed?

38. Are your necklines and cuffs clean?

39. Do you use a clothes brush to remove lint?

40. Are your closet and drawers neat?

41. Is your purse well-organized and clean?

42. When changing clothes, do you hang them up immediately or put them aside to be washed?

43. Do you have lingerie in which you feel special?

44. Do you protect your good clothes from perspiration stains and odor? In the past, we had dress shields that fit into the armhole of good clothes for that.

45. Do your clothes fit? Are they comfortable? Are shoulder and waist seams, hem, and sleeve lengths where they belong?

46. Have you learned to shop alone, confident in your knowledge of yourself?

47. Are you getting enough rest and sleep?

48. Are you comfortable about your appearance in the presence of prominent and well-dressed people?

49. Do you check yourself carefully in front of a full-length, three-way mirror, observing all details, front, side, and back with a small hand mirror?

50. Do you remember to smile, inviting others to smile and reinforcing your own happy attitude?

"Since your class, I feel I've blossomed. I have beautiful colors to work with, my makeup looks much better, my hair is more fun. Your class helped me feel much better about myself! Thanks!"
—Janet Roberts

The Winning Look of Makeup

Long ago I abandoned the over-simplistic "face shape" theory. Faces don't neatly fall into shapes. Faces must be defined in three sections—forehead area, nose area, and mouth/chin area. We individually analyze each area then create makeup and a hairstyle to bring balance to that area. Christy Brinkley is a perfect example. Her face has strong square lines until her chin which is pointed.

Also, I don't always work to create an oval face. A strong square face, such as Christy Brinkley or Sophia Loren is a beauty attribute to be featured, not blended into a common shape. So whenever I find an unusual quality on a woman's face, I work to highlight and bring it forward. The following photos focus on makeup effects.

Once you know how to use color and makeup, you can improve the way you look. Herein, you'll see women of all ages, from every race, in makeup in their color and applied for their structure. With these easy patterns, each woman can do her own makeup at home. So with each photograph, look for tips and tricks you can apply to yourself.

Remember that makeup should always present the real you more beautifully. It should never be the main attraction. *These women are not models, not actresses, they are real women like you and me.*

Note: most makeover books show models airbrushed along with highly involved contouring techniques. Because this book is for real women, busy and contributing like you, we've kept the makeup from ten to twenty minutes or less, similar to the time you have to do your makeup at home. Focus on the before and after effects.

The Beauty Code

Aquamarine

BlueGreen

Deluxe Cosmetic Case contains:

Top Mini Tray—A
> *Blush Colors*— Aire, Dawn Pink, Aurora
> *Highlight Shadow*—Whisper Pink

Main Top Tray—B
> *Contour Eyeshadow*—
> Fawn Mist
> *Eyeshadows*—Cream,
> Woodland Green, Rose Glow,
> Sheer Coral, Sea Nymph,
> Peacock, Champagne,
> Cameo Frost;
> Extra options: Chamois,
> Coral Kiss, Lilac, Mint,
> Morning Sky, Rose Mist, Sunrise
> *Perfect Match Foundation*— Cashew, Almond
> *2 Lipstick Colors*—Primrose, Cantaloupe;
> Extra options: Barely Dawn, Blossom, Bud Pink, Coral
> Creme, Misty Melon, Petal Glacè, Sheer Red, Shrimp
> *2 Lip Liners*—Sherry, Taupe; Extra Options:
> Coral, Touch
> *1 Eyeliner*—Kohl Brown;
> Extra options: Medium Brown, Forest Green,
> Peacock, Platinum Brown
> *1 Mascara*—Brown Black
> *Applicators*—2 Eyeshadow Sponges;
> 1 Foundation Sponge

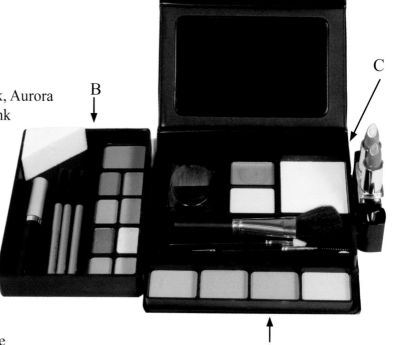

Color Planner
My Beauty Code™

Bottom Tray—C
> *Translucent Pan Powder*—with cloth powder puff
> *Lid Primer Disguise*: Light
> *Crème Blush*—Peaches 'n Creme
> *Brushes*—Brow Groomer/Chisel Brush
> Medium Sable Blush/Powder Brush
> Small Sable Blush Brush

Cosmetic Collection

Sapphire

BluePurple

Deluxe Cosmetic Case contains:
Top Mini Tray—A
Blush Colors—Amethyst, Heather, Ambience
Highlight Shadow—Whisper Pink

Main Top Tray—B
Contour Eyeshadow—Night Dove
Eyeshadows— Haze, Mauvessence, Dew, Midnight, Violet Kiss, Thistledown, Taupe, Dusk;
Extra options: Ashes of Roses, Azalea Mist,
Ice Blue,Myrtle, Shimmer Pink
Perfect Match Foundation—Cashew, Mauvewood, Sapphire Sun
2 Lipstick Colors—Dresden, Blackberry Frost; Extra options: Festival Pink, Heather, Mauve Glacè, Monet, Pink Glacè, Pink Shimmer, Pink Silk, Plum, Plum Glacè, Pure Mauve, Rosemond, Winterberry
2 Lip Liners—Mauve, Taupe Lip Definer
Extra options: Burgundy, Grape, Raspberry
1 Eyeliner—Kohl Brown; Extra options: Medium Brown, Black, Navy,
1 Mascara—Black, Brown Black
Applicators—2 Eyeshadow Sponges; 1 Foundation Sponge

Bottom Tray—C
Translucent Pan Powder—with cloth powder puff
Lid Primer Disguise: Light, Medium, Dark
Crème Blush—Wild Berry
Brushes—Brow Groomer/Chisel Brush
Medium Sable Blush/Powder Brush
Small Sable Blush Brush

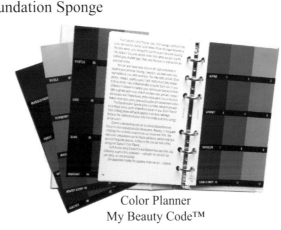

Color Planner
My Beauty Code™

Ruby
RedPurple

Deluxe Cosmetic Case contains:

Top Mini Tray—A

Blush Colors—Dahlia, Chateau, Grape Mist
Highlight Shadow—Oyster

Main Top Tray—B

Contour Eyeshadow—Smoke;
Extra options: Night Dove
Eyeshadows—Early Wine, Evening
Orchid, Azalea Mist, Geisha,
Indigo, Mulberry, Myrtle, Taupe,
Extra options: Black Pearl, Dusk,
Eggplant, Plum Dust, Renaissance
Blue, Sheer Silver
Perfect Match Foundation—Pearl
Bisque, Teakwood, Dusk, Minque
2 Lipstick Colors—Hawthorne, Sangria;
Extra options: Currant, Fuchsia, Grape, Islander, Plum Glacè, Plum Wine,
Raspberry Ice, Toreador Red
2 Lip Liners—Grape, Taupe;
Extra options: Burgundy, Grape, Toreador Red, Touch
1 Eyeliner—Black; Extra options: Charcoal, Kohl Brown, Myrtle, Smoke
1 Mascara—Black
Applicators—2 Eyeshadow Sponges;
1 Foundation Sponge

Bottom Tray—C

Translucent Pan Powder—with cloth
powder puff
Lid Primer Disguise: Light, Medium, Dark
Crème Blush—Grecian Wine
Brushes—Brow Groomer/Chisel Brush
Medium Sable Blush/Powder Brush
Small Sable Blush Brush

Color Planner
My Beauty Code™

Garnet
RedOrange

Deluxe Cosmetic Case contains:
Top Mini Tray—A

Blush Colors— Russet Spice, Auburn, Chestnut
Highlight Shadow—Oatmeal

Main Top Tray—B

Contour Eyeshadow—
Russian Sable
Eyeshadows—Aztec Gold, Moss,
Mahogany, Raisin, Chamois,
Mikado Blue, Sunset, Clay;
Extra options: Chocolate,
Cinnabar, Harvest Plum
Perfect Match Foundation—
India Ivory, Mahogany, Warm Umber, Mocha
2 Lipstick Colors—Autumn Rose, Warm Brandy;
Extra options: Almond Glacè, Antique Rose, Bordeaux,
Brick, Burnt Poppy, Cappuccino, Gaucho Red, Malibu,
Rustique, Sunset Glacè
2 Lip Liners—Mocha, Light Brown;
Extra options: Braisen, Choco-Latte, Java
1 Eyeliner—Kohl Brown
Extra options: Black, Chocolate, Teal
1 Mascara—Black
Applicators—2 Eyeshadow Sponges;
1 Foundation Sponge

Bottom Tray—C
*Translucent Pan Powde*r—with cloth powder puff
Lid Primer Disguise: Light, Medium, Dark
Crème Blush—Cinnamon
Brushes—Brow Groomer/Chisel Brush
Medium Sable Blush/Powder Brush
Small Sable Blush Brush

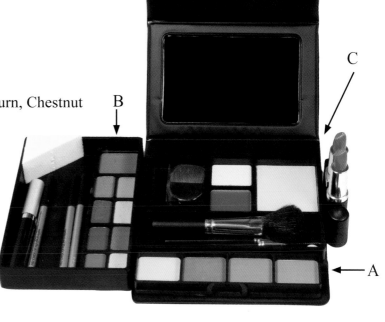

Color Planner
My Beauty Code™

Topaz
Yellow Orange

Deluxe Cosmetic Case contains:

Top Mini Tray—A
Blush Colors—Italian Earth, Sandstone, Mango
Highlight Shadow—Wheat

Main Top Tray—B
Contour Eyeshadow—Walnut
Eyeshadows—Aztec Gold, Cheyenne, Chutney, Khaki, Peacock, Sienna, Sierra Sun, Tobacco; Extra options: Bronzed, Camel, Pumpkin,
Perfect Match Foundation—Pistachio, Topaz, Pecan
2 Lipstick Colors— Terra Cotta, Persian Copper; Extra options: Caramel Crème, Chili Pepper, Paprika, Peach Glaze, Smoked Salmon, Spice, Sunset Glacè, Toast
2 Lip Liners—Castilian, Light Brown; Extra Options: Coppercino, Java, Walnut
1 Eyeliner—Walnut; Extra Options: Khaki, Kohl Brown
1 Mascara—Brown Black
Applicators—2 Eyeshadow Sponges; 1 Foundation Sponge

Bottom Tray—C
Translucent Pan Powder—with cloth powder puff
Lid Primer Disguise: Light, Medium, Dark
Crème Blush—Ginger Spice
Brushes—Brow Groomer/Chisel Brush
Medium Sable Blush/Powder Brush
Small Sable Blush Brush

Color Planner
My Beauty Code™

The Beauty Code™ Compact

The three-tiered black luxury washable makeup case is 6.5" by 5" by 2.25". Each tray is tooled to fit together tightly, which ensures that it will travel well. It includes a mirror and a long Velcro closure to keep your cosmetics secure. Individual compartments hold eyeshadow, blush, and powder. Each can hold two pans if you want to have a backup of your favorite, most used colors.

Peridot

Yellow Green

Deluxe Cosmetic Case contains:
Top Mini Tray—A
Blush Colors—Peach, Nectar, Maple Sugar
Highlight Shadow—Champagne

Main Top Tray—B
Contour Eyeshadow—Warm Spice
Eyeshadows—Sheer Coral,
Sunset, Banana, Peacock,
Chamois, Chutney, Willow,
Lichen; Extra options:
Lime, Ming Green, Toast,
Sea Nymph, Shimmer Sun
Perfect Match Foundation—
Pistachio or Sandlewood
2 Lipstick Colors—
Brownberry, Shimmer Peach;
Extra options: Almond Glacè,
Apricot Crème, Nasturtium, Peach Glaze,
Persimmon, Spun Honey
2 Lip Liners—Sherry, Light Brown
Optional: Cider, Spice, Tangerine
1 Eyeliner—Walnut
Optional: Khaki, Kohl Brown, Medium Brown, Peacock
1 Mascara—Brown Black
Applicators—2 Eyeshadow Sponges;
1 Foundation Sponge

Bottom Tray—C
*Translucent Pan Powde*r—with cloth powder puff
Lid Primer Disguise: Light
Crème Blush—Maple Creme
Brushes—Brow Groomer/Chisel Brush
Medium Sable Blush/Powder Brush
Small Sable Blush Brush

Color Planner
My Beauty Code™

Garnet
RedOrange

Warm, rich coloring invites you to Brenda. We increased the depth and warmth of her eyes with dark shadow blended over her lid and up into a medium tone on her frontal bone. We brought blush onto the front of her cheek to shorten the lower part of her face. Rich, full lip color supports her pretty lip line. Then we put blush on the upper, outside edge of her neck to both strengthen her jawline and cut the length of her neck. She has the perfect forehead to wear her hair off her face. See Fig. 83, 99C, 100 in Chapter 7.

BRENDA

Sapphire
BluePurple

Here we wanted to feature Lindsay's already strong, lovely face. Makeup artist, Jocelyn Brown contoured Lindsay's eyes to increase their size and width. She added fascination with depth and mixed color shadows. Jocelyn softened the edges of Lindsay's forehead and supported her already lovely mouth by contouring her lips with three colors—first a soft taupe lip liner, next basic lip color, Dresden, then a highlight color on the inside edge. See Fig. 82, 100, 99A in Chapter 7.

Jocelyn Brown
Makeup Artist

152

LINDSAY

SANDY

Aquamarine
BlueGreen

A light and fun personality, our goal with Sandy was to increase the size and depth of her eyes without overpowering them. We did this with medium brown shadow on her outer lids that moved in soft tones up into her frontal bone. We gave contour to her cheeks with a youthful pattern. We enlarged and intensified her lips with light, bright lipstick combinations so we maintained her light, fun feeling. The soft browns, cream, and corals in the Blue Green Collection allowed us to easily achieve this for Sandy. Her pert hair style works well for her in every way. See Fig. 85, 92, 97, 99B in Chapter 7.

Sapphire
BluePurple

Jessica Victor, Jeannie's makeup artist, used highlight to remove dark circles and deep lines from Jeannie's face. She then focused on accenting and contouring Jeannie's eyes. She used blushes from the BP collection to give more contour and definition to Jeannie's cheek area plus she filled in and enlarged Jeannie's lips to support her pretty smile. Jessica gave Jeannie this stunning new hairstyle which strengthened Jeannie's jawline and updated her hairstyle to give her a new, younger look. See Fig. 87, 99C, 104 in Chapter 7.

Jessica Victor
Makeup Artist

JEANNIE

Sapphire
BluePurple

A professional woman with soft coloring, Ann's look earns respect and recognition. We had to carefully intensify her features without overpowering them. We chose from a range of medium and light colors to enlarge and contour her deep set eyes and then just lightly defined her brows. We gave more definition to the apple of her cheeks and her pretty lip line. We directed her hair low in the forehead and out in the eye, cheek and jaw area to focus on her eyes and widen her cheek area while framing her jawline. See Fig. 85, 89, 90, 99A, and 100 in Chapter 7.

ANN

Sapphire
BluePurple

Our overall goal with Susan was to create a balance to her lovely face using color in a soft circle from her eyes to cheeks to mouth. Her deep set eyes and low brows require lightly defining her brows, contouring her eyelids and defining the shape of her eyes with medium to light shadows. Anything very dark on her brows or eyes would set her eyes even deeper. We placed her blush on the outside edge of her face and used a clear, rich color lipstick with a highlighter color on the inside to bring her lips forward. See Fig. 85, 90, 99A, 102 in Chapter 7.

SUSAN

KELLY

Ruby
RedPurple

Kelly's striking intense coloring allowed us to use darker, more vibrant colors on her. First, we shortened her high forehead with soft brown powder and blush. We added curvature to her eyes with dark shadow on the inside and outside of her eyelids, lighter colors on the middle. A diagonal blush pattern breaks the roundness of her cheeks. Her brighter lip colors focus your attention on her pretty mouth. We directed her hair style slightly out in the eye area to balance her more narrow forehead with the bottom of her face which is wider. See Fig. 87, 100 in Chapter 7.

Ruby
RedPurple

Her many even and pretty features made Brittany an enjoyable model. We visually shortened her forehead with soft brown contour powder and then accented her pretty up-slant eyes with dark to medium shadows. Next, we placed her blush on the outside edges of her cheeks to add width in the cheekbone area. Finally, we used a taupe then a grape lip liner to enlarge her top lip, added a bright strong color to feature her pretty lip line and finished with a highlight color to add curve to her bottom lip. This gave a finished look to her lips without giving them too much emphasis which *keeps* the emphasis on her eyes. See Fig. 80, 83, 104 in Chapter 7.

BRITTANY

JODI

Ruby
RedPurple

One of my favorite makeovers, Jodi has beautiful contours in her eyes, cheeks, mouth, and chin. The trick was to feature them without making them look too round. We gave curve and depth to her eyes using both dark and medium eyeshadows accented by black liner. Now her dark eyes sparkle. To feature the apple of her cheeks, we used diagonal blush patterns that curved at the bottom. We first extended her lip line with Taupe and Grape lip liner, then used strong rich lip color highlighted with a pearl lipstick to give more fullness and projection to her mouth. See Fig. 87, 83, 102 in Chapter 7.

Ruby
RedPurple

Another favorite makeover, Melissa just came alive with her makeup. We softened the corner of her forehead then took a strong diagonal bang to cut its width. Next we focus your attention on her amazing eyes by adding curve to her lid and extending the width with stronger dark colors on the outside edge. This enlarges the apparent size of her eyes. Her diagonal blush pattern curves to accentuate the apple of her cheek. Finally, full rich lip colors draw your eyes to her pretty smile. These lip colors and flip in her hair fill in her narrow jawline. See Fig. 83, 99A, and 100 in Chapter 7.

156

MELISSA

EVA

Garnet
RedOrange

A gracious lady, we accented Eva's pretty, large eyes with dark liner and mascara, only softy shadowed her eyelids which are deep set enough on their own. Also, we softly finished her brow to frame, but not overpower, her eyes. A diagonal blush pattern outlines her naturally lovely cheek contours and brings your attention right to her beautiful smile. The diagonal side lines of her hair, as well as the V-neckline in her 'before' photo, cut the square corners of her jawline. See Fig. 84, 99A, 100 in Chapter 7.

Garnet
RedOrange

Vivacious and fun, we opened Kristina's eye area by enlarging and widening her spirited eyes with dark upper lid shadows, eyeliner, and mascara. By bringing her blush up on the outside edge of her face by her eyes, we continued to feature and open her eye area which also balanced the top and bottom halves of her face. Her lip colors finish her mouth to feature her smile without adding projection. We contoured her bottom lip with dark color on the outside and bottom edge then used highlight color on the center for fullness. See Fig. 80, 83, 99D, and 100 in Chapter 7.

KRISTINA

KENDRA

Topaz
YellowOrange

Kendra moved into smart sophistication with her new makeup and hair style. Warm, inviting colors tempt you to linger on her face. We accented her large eyes with dark lid shadows, eyeliner, and mascara. We used the cheek pattern you find in Fig. 91 B, but extended it to the edge of her cheeks to widen them a bit. We wanted to keep the attention up on her eyes, so we just finished her mouth with softer colors. We also strengthened her jawline by adding blush to the top sides of her neck. See Fig. 83, 102 in Chapter 7.

Sapphire
BluePurple

Kaylee's sister, Keisha's is a cosmetologist. She completed both Kaylee's makeup and hairstyle using Kaylee's Beauty Code Color Palette, Blue Purple. Her soft brown eyeshadows make her eyes look larger and give them warmth and depth. Keisha used a soft diagonal blush pattern to bring your eyes to Kaylee's mouth which Keisha then finished in soft pastel lip colors in keeping with Kaylee's gentle look and coloring. Her hairstyle framed and strengthened her jawline. See Fig. 80, 87,83, 99C, 101 in Chapter 7.

Keisha Black
Makeup Artist

KAYLEE

158

LISA

Ruby
RedPurple

A talented, professional woman, we supported Lisa's credibility in her look. We cut Lisa's forehead length and still lengthened her face with soft, separated bangs and blush at the top of her forehead. We gently brought her eyes, cheeks and mouth out more to the edge of her face using an eyeshadow pattern wider at the outside edge of

her eye, a diagonal cheek pattern on the outside of her cheek area. We added width to her lip line with Taupe and Grape lip liner. Diagonal patterns in her hair and blush counteract the round lines in her face. See Fig. 83, 100, 99A in Chapter 7.

Ruby
RedPurple

Chiseled features in her jaw, chin, forehead, and nose set Nicole's face apart. Makeup artist, Brooke Bunker, Nicole's sister, accented Nicole's eyes by adding depth to her lids and at the outside edge of her eyes. A soft diagonal blush pattern lengthens her shorter cheekbone area to balance the longer forehead and jawline areas of her face. Brooke featured Nicole's beautiful smile and lip line with rich full colors to complete her look. By cutting and styling her hair fuller on the sides and curving softly at her jawline, Brooke framed Nicole's striking face structure. See Fig. 90, 96, 99D, 100 in Chapter 7.

Brooke Bunker
Makeup Artist

NICOLE

LILY

Ruby
RedPurple

Her makeup really brought out the quiet gentle beauty of this lovely lady. We gave curve and depth to her eye area with soft, medium shadow on the outside and inside of her eyelid. We highlighted under her brow and right above the pupil of her eye. Then we contoured her cheeks using a diagonal blush pattern with two colors, a bright color to feature her beautiful high cheek bones and a deeper blush color to give her cheeks depth. Her mouth is perfect; we added color to give it curve and irresistible appeal. See Fig. 87, 91, 100 in Chapter 7.

Garnet
RedOrange

Inviting large eyes, a warm smile, Denise proves beauty doesn't belong only to the young. We shortened her forehead slightly with blush and irregular bangs. We moved to focus on her eyes with added depth on her lower lid using darker shadow, liner, and mascara. We lengthened her cheek area slightly with a diagonal blush pattern that curved beneath the apple of her cheeks to spotlight that feature. We finished her look by defining her lip line with walnut and mocha lip liner, Warm Brandy lip color and Autumn Rose highlight. See Fig. 82, 93, 94, 104 in Chapter 7.

160

DENISE

KRISTEN

Peridot
YellowGreen

Fun and friendly, we shortened Kristen's long forehead with soft, irregular bangs that still allowed her face to look longer. Her hairstyle allows for easy upkeep. We gave her more width at the outside edge of her eyeshadow pattern to enlarge her eyes. We used only a bit of color on the inside of her eyes due to lower space between her eye and brow. A diagonal cheek pattern cut the roundness of her cheeks. We finished with Light

Brown and Sherry lip liners to widen her lips and bright lip colors to strengthen her pretty smile. See Fig. 86, 84, 91A, 94 in Chapter 7.

Topaz
YellowOrange

An all-around good friend and mom, Laura needs natural, quick, and easy in both hair and makeup. We used just a bit of eyeshadow on the outside lid as well as the outside edge of her eyes to feature her smiling eyes. A simple, straight across blush pattern cuts the apparent length of her face. The basic lip color, Terra Cotta, outlines and defines her lips. Highlight lip color, Almond Glacè, pumps a sense of fullness into her bottom lip and supports her great smile. Her hair style is simple with stacked fullness that fills out her thin face and keeps her hair style easy to manage. See Fig. 85, 99D, 101 in Chapter 7.

LAURA

Aquamarine
BlueGreen

Spirited and inventive, Katy has beautiful chiseled jaw and chin structure. We first applied soft brown blush powder to shorten her forehead then intensified her eyes with strong dark liners on her eyelids blended with medium eyeshadows. To make her eyes look larger, we brought her eyeshadows up and out on the outside edge. By placing blush on the outside edge of her cheeks, we opened up and widened her face and eye area. We finished with a medium lipstick highlighted to add fullness and curve to her bottom lip. See Fig. 84, 99D, 101 in Chapter 7.

KATY

Aquamarine
BlueGreen

We enhanced Colette's pretty coloring and face shape with soft blush at the top of her forehead, thinned on the edge of her eye and curved down on to her cheeks. This framed her eyes. To make her eyes look larger, we brought medium eyeshadow out and up on the outside edge, then rounded it up and over the top lid to meet and blend into the highlight area under her brow. Perfectly shaped, we finished her lips with clear, bright colors similar to those we used throughout her make-over to maintain Collette's appealing, youthful look. See Fig 80, 91, 99B, 100 in Chapter 7.

COLLETTE

Sapphire
BluePurple

We added warmth and depth to focus attention on Paige's sparkling eyes. We used dark liner smudged with Night Dove eyeshadow to intensify her lid. Then we extended her shadow on the outside edge to make her eyes look larger. Blush in a straighter pattern on the outside edges of her cheeks and the top of her forehead opens and widens her face and eye area. We chose darker, rich lip colors which brought focus to her mouth.

We used a lighter lip color on the inside of her bottom lip to give it a more full and curved appearance. See Fig. 91D, 101 in Chapter 7.

PAIGE

Sapphire
BluePurple

A true high brow, Lexi has space for a lot of eyeshadow. Careful so as to not overpower her soft coloring, we layered shadow moving from medium dark on her lids to medium then medium light on her frontal bone up to the highlight just under her brows. We brought her eyeshadow out on the outside edge to widen her eyes and balance her eye with the outer width of her face. We feature her perfect mouth with rich medium lip color and lighter lip color on the inside of her bottom lip. Gentle blush gives her the glow of good health. See Fig 82, 89, 83, 99B in Chapter 7.

LEXI

Peridot
YellowGreen

Looking at Kay, you really see the glow that you get from wearing the right colors. We defined and finished her eyes with medium brown powder, intensified right next to her lashes with smudged walnut eyeliner. This put the focus on her smiling eyes without making them heavy because of her fair coloring. We contoured her cheeks with peach tones to feature their pretty apple shape and gave her a healthy glow. A soft blend of peaches and soft orange finished her mouth. Light, bright, and effervescent, Kay's a lovely lady with a lovely look simply done by using her right colors. See Fig. 80, 90, 92, 99B, 101-103 in Chapter 7.

KAY

Garnet
RedOrange

Keeping her look as natural as possible, we first shortened her high forehead with soft brown contour powder. Then we lightly finished her brows with contour powder. Next we added depth and curve to her eye lids with dark shadow on the outside edges and light shadow in the middle. We used a soft diagonal blush pattern and diagonal side design lines in her hair style to cut the square lines of her jaw. We then highlighted her jawline by adding blush at the top sides of her neck. We finished her look with bright, clear lip colors. See Fig. 82, 99A, 100 in Chapter 7.

164

GINGER

ANDREA

Garnet
RedOrange

This natural town and country look serves Andrea's beauty well. As a busy math major, she wanted a simple routine. We groomed her brows so all she has to do is brush them in place. We intensified her eyes with smudged liner at the base of her top and bottom lashes then blended her eyeshadow pattern up, out and down around the outside edge of her eye. A diagonal blush pattern contours and cuts the width of her cheek, keeps attention at her eye and gives her a soft healthy glow. Rich lip color finishes her mouth and presents her beautiful smile. See Fig. 80, 88, 99A, 100 in Chapter 7.

Garnet
RedOrange

Here we increased the intensity and apparent size of Erica's eyes with rich full brown eyeshadow blended on the lid and around the outer edge of her eyes as well as up in a beautiful shape on the outer edge of her frontal bone. We placed blush more to the outside edge of her cheeks to keep the focus on her eyes. As easy finish, we defined her already lovely mouth with dark and light colors to give her lips more contour. Erica is another lady who benefited from a bit of blush on the outside top edges of her neck to strengthen her jawline. See Fig. 80, 87, 99D, 100 in Chapter 7.

ERICA

BECKY

Ruby
RedPurple

Naturally lovely, we added depth to increase the warmth of Becky's inviting eyes. A diagonal blush pattern leads you to her amazing optimistic lip line and softens the edge of her square jawline. To widen her lips, we simply lined her lip further to the edge, filled in with medium dark lip color, then used a lighter lip color in the middle to give her lips a fuller, more curved appearance. The bit of irregularity to her bangs lets you see to the top of her forehead, which lengthens her face. See Fig. 80, 99A, 101 in Chapter 7.

Sapphire
BluePurple

With medium dark hair, Alex is a great Blue Purple example. She has distinct features so all she needs is stronger eye makeup to draw you into her soft, dewy eyes. We groomed and shaped her brows then "set" them with clear mascara. I used a smudged eyeliner effect right next to her lashes top and bottom, then blended Night Dove contour color up onto her frontal bone in a full wing pattern. Her clear, soft lip colors finish her lips but don't compete with her eyes. A long, diagonal blush pattern slims and balances both the width and length of her face. See Fig. 80, 89, 91, 99B, 100 in Chapter 7.

ALEX

CLAUDIA

Garnet
RedOrange

A striking woman, Claudia's makeover moved her to an amazing look. We contoured her forehead and directioned her hair out to balance her forehead to her fuller jawline. We added depth to her beautiful dark eyes with strong dark colors on the lid, around the edges and down onto the bottom lid. We accented the apple of her cheeks with a diagonal blush pattern that also made her jawline appear thinner. Full, rich lip color finished her look. See Fig. 85, 99A, 103 in Chapter 7.

Sapphire
BluePurple

Light, airy, and feminine all describe Taunya. You'd hardly believe she's a mother. We kept this effervescent look with light soft colors in her makeup. We contoured her frontal bone with shadow on the inner and outer corners. She benefited from a wider shadow pattern on the outside edge of her eye. We also kept her blush stronger on the outside edge to open and widen her cheek bone area. Bright, clear makeup colors defined her mouth and finished her look. Blush at the top of her forehead and irregular bangs gave her face balance. See Fig. 86, 99B, 101 in Chapter 7.

TAUNYA

LINDSAY

Topaz
YellowOrange

Lindsay's face says "I'm ready for adventure." We kept her colors bright and clear to keep her natural look. Medium and dark eyeshadows defined and gave depth to her eyes with a pattern that extended slightly at the outside edge which made her eyes look bigger. Straighter blush patterns on the outside edge of her face widened her cheekbone area and kept attention up near her eyes.

Light, colored gloss gave her mouth a finished look without making her look made up. See Fig. 82, 88, 91, 101 in Chapter 7.

Sapphire
BluePurple

Notice how her soft hair styling around her jawline slimmed and balanced that area of her face. Her amazing large eyes capture you. We gave them depth and a dewy feeling with medium and soft eyeshadows lifting them at the outside edge. Long in the cheek bone area of her face, we used blush to cut the apparent length in that area. By adding a blend of feminine pink lipsticks, we put attention on her mouth, projecting it to take attention away from her chin as does the soft hair design around the lower bottom of her face and neck. This completed her look. See Fig. 93, 99C, 101 in Chapter 7.

168

ASHLEY

CHRISTINA

Ruby
RedPurple

A stunning example of the gamin look, Christina's makeup colors perfectly present her amazing coloring. Her chiseled haircut features her face structure and keeps your focus on her eyes. To emphasize both her eyes and high cheekbones, we started her blush high on the sides then moved her blush in a diagonal pattern to both contour her cheeks and bring you to her captivating lip line where both her lips meet. We used muted light lip color to give a finished look

to her lips. A bit of artistic irregularity in her brows captured lingering interest there before you melt into her eyes. See Fig. 80, 89, 99A, 103 in Chapter 7.

Sapphire
BluePurple

We used light shadow powder to bring Sara's deep set eyes forward, then intensified them with dark eyeliner smudged around the edge of both the upper and lower lid next to her lashes. Light brown powder finished her low brows. Her blush pattern was a balancing trick. It needed to stay just inside the outer edge so as not to widen her face in the cheekbone area but not move too much to the center which would close it in. Her lively smile is highlighted with clear bright colors in keeping with the overall intensity of her coloring. Structurally, Sara benefits from a longer hairstyle and a cooler hair color. See Fig. 80, 85, 88, 85, 100 in Chapter 7.

SARA

BEKAH

Sapphire
BluePurple

A pretty young teen, Bekah looks and acts older than she is. We wanted to bring her eyes forward and widen them to balance the top third of her face to the bottom two-thirds. So we added depth to her eyes with dark liner smudged with lighter browns to intensify them without overpowering them. We then brought her eyeshadow pattern up and out more on the sides. We used a youthful blush pattern of clear bright tones and a medium lipstick to finish her look. See Fig. 89, 86, 99B, 101-103 in Chapter 7.

Sapphire
BluePurple

An early consultant with our early company, Signairé, Janine was a student in my Consultant Training and Color Mastery Program. She helped with some makeovers for this book. Here she gave contour and depth to her eyes by lifting and extending her shadow pattern which made her eyes look larger and balanced her eyes with the outside edge of her face. She's kept her blush on the outside of her face to keep the cheekbone area open. She stopped your eye travel with vivid lip color on her pretty mouth. See Fig. 80, 86, 100 in Chapter 7.

170

JANINE

JESSICA

Ruby
RedPurple

Beautiful, dark, and feminine, Jessica's dark coloring allows full, vibrant colors in her makeup. We still can not overpower her eyes which are small in comparison to her face. We've made her eyes look larger by extending her eyeshadow pattern up and out at the sides. Then we brought her blush pattern from the bottom edge of the apple of her cheeks up to the outer edge of her eyes to focus attention there. Her flawless skin captivates you with how it accepts color. Beautiful lip colors compliment her lovely mouth. See Fig. 80, 86, 84, 87, 99C, 100 in Chapter 7.

Topaz
YellowOrange

To enlarge Michelle's eyes, we used a light shadow to bring them forward then smudged dark eyeliner right next to her lashes to intensify the lid. This added warmth and focus on her eyes. We extended her blush pattern up to the outside edge of her eyes and onto the front of her cheeks to balance her cheekbone area with her eyes. Then we put bright, clear lip colors on her to keep your focus on the center of her face. Her hairstyle allows you to see to the top of her face, then it fills in around her neck to frame and strengthen her jawline. See Fig. 85, 84, 87, 100 in Chapter 7.

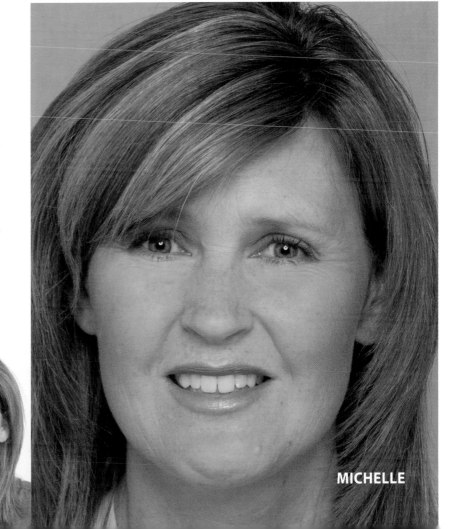

MICHELLE

Sapphire
BluePurple

The Beauty Code™ makeup colors gave Karen's already pretty face just that extra bit of definition she needed to make her sparkle and glow. We added a bit of brown powder to define her naturally lovely brows then we blended dark eyeshadow up onto her frontal bone and over to just above her iris to give curve and intensity to her eyes. A soft outside edge blush pattern connected her eye area to her pretty mouth which we finished in a rich outside lip color and a brighter, clear inside color. This gave curve to her lips. See Fig. 80, 86, pattern 99B placed on the outside of her cheek, 100 in Chapter 7.

KAREN

Garnet
RedOrange

Andrea carries a great natural look head to toe. We wanted to keep her look of glowing health with the barest makeup—well blended. We used a light blush to shorten her forehead at the top. Next, we intensified her amazing brown eyes with dark Kohl liner smudged with Russian Sable eyeshadow and took the pattern out from the outer edge of her eye, down and around to the bottom lid. To widen her cheek area to balance with her jawline, we kept her blush on the outside edge of her face.

We finished her lips in soft clear tones. See Fig. 86, 84,92, 99D, 100 in Chapter 7.

172

ANDREA

SHELLI

Ruby
RedPurple

A beautiful young woman, we brought Shelli's eyes forward and out with intense black liner and smudge eyeshadow blended from the last line to the outer edge of her eye. We brought her blush up to the outer edge of her eyes to focus and softly widen her eye area. Blush at the top outside edges of her neck strengthens the sides of her jawline and balances her chin. A pretty mix of lip colors contour her mouth presenting her winning smile. Her softly styled dark hair works well for her long neck to complete her look. See Fig. 80, 86, 88, 87, 91B, 92 in Chapter 7.

Ruby
RedPurple

Strong, beautiful features, Jessica changed her hair color moving her from a Red Purple to a Red Orange palette. This lightened and intensified the brown color in her eyes. We used the Ruby Red Purple makeup because the colors worked better with the tones of her face. But we softened it to not clash with her hair. We intensified on and around her eye lids with dark liner smudged with eyeshadow then blended the pattern up and out. A diagonal cheek pattern forward on her face cuts the length of her cheekbone area. Rich colors finished her lips. See Fig. 80, 86, 99A in Chapter 7.

JESSICA

STACY

Garnet
RedOrange

Stacy's polished look supports her as a professional woman. We widened and filled in her eyeshadow pattern on the outside edge to balance her eyes with her brow bone line. Her diagonal blush pattern visually shortened the length of her cheekbone area. Then we placed blush on the top outside edges of her neck to both contour her neck and strengthen her jawline. We used strong lip liner to the outer edge of her lips and filled in her lips with strong lip colors which widened her smile and featured the pretty line of her top lip. See Fig. 80, 84, 87, 99A, 102 in Chapter 7.

Ruby
RedPurple

Gentle loveliness with chiseled bone structure, Adrienne is an accomplished musician. We filled in the large space between her eyelids and her eyebrows with gradients of Black Pearl, Night Dove and Hawaiian Orchid eyeshadows lighter in the middle and darker on the outer and inner edge of the pattern. The diagonal cheek pattern forward on her face brings your eyes to her pretty mouth which we finished in rich full colors. See Fig. 82, 87, 89, 91, 99A in Chapter 7.

ADRIENNE

STEPHANIE

Sapphire
BluePurple

Effervescent, Stephanie keeps things moving and alive. Her face balance is shorter on top, longer on the bottom especially with her lovely long neck. We used several methods to cut the lower length of her face and neck, including her hair lines and a blush pattern that cut in and around her jawline. We contoured her lips with blended strong colors to stop your eye travel. We intensified her smiling eyes with dark Kohl liner smudged with Night Dove and Thistledown eyeshadow. See Fig. 82, 83, 85, 99B, 100 in Chapter 7.

Ruby
RedPurple

We intensified Kehau's exotic dark eyes with smudged dark liner and a shadow pattern that moves up and out in gradients of mixed Black Pearl, Eggplant and a touch of Geisha. We kept her blush pattern on the outside edge of her face to open up her cheek bone area. Her lip color brings all her features into a soft circle. With her too, we placed blush on the top out-side edges of her neck to both contour her neck and strengthen her jawline. See Fig. 80, 86, 91, 103 in Chapter 7.

KEHAU

GINA

Sapphire
BluePurple

A soft, feminine beauty, Gina has a strong sense of fashion and style. To intensify her eyes, we used medium tones darker at the lash line, but never too strong. Her strong lid line must be countered with an up line in her eyeshadow to keep her look happy. We kept her blush on the outside edge of her face in a straighter pattern to cut the length of her face. This opened up her cheekbone area. A soft blend of muted and highlight lip colors finished her pretty mouth. She successfully uses long, airy earrings to fill in between her ears and jawline. See Fig. 89, 83, 99D, 100 in Chapter 7.

Ruby
RedPurple

Even though young, Aspen is one who has deep waters. We kept her youthful look with soft fresh colors—soft subtle eyeshadows on the outside and inside corners of her eye. We kept her blush on the outside edge of her cheek to open her cheekbone area. Then we contoured her mouth with clear lip colors blended to finish her look. See Fig. 80, 87, 95 in Chapter 7.

ASPEN

SUSIE

Garnet
RedOrange

Bold and dark eyed, we brought out Susie's beauty with her rich Red Orange makeup colors. We used a strong uplift line in her eyeshadow pattern in rich Russian Sable and Moss Green. We kept her blush pattern up near her eye to fill in the outside edge of her face. Then we moved the blush in diagonal patterns which featured her lovely cheek bones and framed the apple of her cheeks—definite beauty features. Strong, bold lip colors kept and finished her deep warm look. See Fig. 89, 86, 99C, 101-top lip in Chapter 7.

Peridot
YellowGreen

Another of our few Yellow Green ladies, Carrie needs subtle tones smoothly blended. An important frame for her inviting eyes, I shaped her brows then used clear mascara to set them. I used Walnut brow powder to define them; Toast and Champagne to contour her upper eyelid. Walnut eyeliner smudged with Lichen visually thickened her lashes along with brown mascara. To fill in the width between her eyes and the outside edge of her face, I brought her blush from the apple of her cheeks up on the outer edge onto her face and onto the top edge of her forehead. To define her lips without too much color, I used Spun Honey over Brownberry. See Fig. 82, 92, 101 top lip, 99A

CARRIE

SHAUNA

Topaz
YellowOrange

Friendly, happy eyes under high brows, Shauna welcomes everyone she meets. We moved her eyeshadows out to the outside edge of her eye which balance her eyes to her cheek and jawline. Again, her colors gave glow and excitement to her face. Blush at the top of her forehead shortened its visual height which helped to keep your focus on her eyes as did her blush which ran high from the outside of her cheek bone. A diagonal blush pattern created an hollow contour to the sides of her cheeks. Clear bright lip color highlighted with a light pearlized inside color completed her engaging smile. See Fig. 80, 83, 87, 99A, 100 in Chapter 7.

Topaz
YellowOrange

A long time client, Janet was a winner in Utah's Ms. Utah Senior America's contest. She also won Utah's Mother and Daughter contest with her daughter Brooke. She believes that knowing how to wear her right colors and styles was an important element in winning those contests. Her hairstyle and "just right" hair color created a feminine and youthful frame for her lovely face. We kept the focus on her eyes with blush high on the sides of her cheeks. Medium brow color and light shadows defined her eyes without overpowering her delicate coloring. Vibrant oranges finished her mouth. See Fig. 82, 90, 99B, 101 in Chapter 7.

DARIA

Aquamarine
BlueGreen

Amazing, strong, and bold bone structure, Daria's face and sculptured cheekbones are meant to be featured. We gave depth and warmth to her eyes with shadow patterns that moved over her lids then around the ends of her eyes and finally fanned up over her lids. A diagonal blush pattern countered the strong square lines in her cheek and jaw while at the same time highlighting them. We used Taupe liner to give more width to her mouth then filled in her lips with clear bright colors in her color collection, Blue Green. See 86, 99A, 102 in Chapter 7.

Garnet
RedOrange

Her own creation, Emily's new hair style set her apart with a "model" look. Her heavy bangs focus you right at her eyes which follow the bang line. We strongly intensified right around her lids to sharpen this striking eye/bang effect. Warm Chestnut blush softly warmed her cheeks and brought up the warmth in her hair color. By mixing strong lip colors with highlight lip colors, we contoured and featured her lips which completed the lovely circle of her features. A fascinating change, don't you agree? See Fig. 82, 99A, 92 in Chapter 7.

EMILY

KARLI

Ruby
RedPurple

Thrilled with her makeover, Karli's large eyes sparkled. They're such a pretty shape, it was fun to shadow along her lid and add depth in her eyelid crease and up onto her frontal bone area. We used a diagonal blush pattern to strengthen her cheekbone area and feature the apple of her cheeks. We then finished her lips in a shade similar to her skin tone so we kept attention on her amazing eyes. See Fig. 80, 93, 99A, 103 in Chapter 7.

Ruby
RedPurple

Tiny, her bold coloring makes you think Haley's bigger and older. We intensified her eyes with black liner to match her brows and hair. Another with lots of space between her eyes and her brows, we balanced Haley's eyeshadow pattern in height and width. We added curve to her lid with lighter color in the middle section and darker colors on both the outside and inside edge. A diagonal blush pattern on the outside of her face opens her cheekbone area and brings you to her lovely mouth which we finished in rich lip colors. See Fig. 80, 91, 99A, 100 in Chapter 7.

180

HALEY

SELINA

Ruby
RedPurple

We took Selina's bangs off her face to open up her large, warm eyes, then further defined them with dark liner smudged with dark eyeshadow on her lid and up onto the outside edge of her frontal bone. Her diagonal blush pattern gently chiseled the square lines in her cheekbone and jaw. We then contoured her lips with darker color which recessed the outside edges and highlighted lip color in the center to add fullness and interest there. See Fig. 80, 93, 99A, bottom lip 103 in Chapter 7.

Sapphire
BluePurple

Bold, square bone structure and contoured cheeks give strength to Nancy's face. We intensified and gave depth to her eyes with dark smudged liner at the lashes and a shadow pattern that filled in around her eyes. We shortened her cheek area with straighter blush patterns that move across the cheeks and finished her lips with a medium rich color. Her straight bang line tends to move her eye area out to balance with the stronger bottom half of her face. See Fig. 80, 87, 99A, 101-top lip in Chapter 7.

NANCY

Sapphire
BluePurple

Soft curls frame Jaci's pretty feminine face. We brought attention up to her eyes with blush. Then we enlarged the look of her eyes with smudged liner and a shadow pattern that moved up onto her frontal bone. This lifted her eye line. Darker shadow on the outside and inside of her lid gave curve to her frontal bone. A diagonal blush pattern contoured her cheeks and moved attention to her pretty mouth. We outlined her lips wider at the outside edge then filled them in with medium color for a natural finished look. See Fig. 89, 101, 99A in Chapter 7.

JACI

Sapphire
BluePurple

A sister to Jaci, Jessica carries an up front, "Let's talk" look. We featured her eyes with medium colors to keep her look natural. We moved her shadow pattern out from the edge of her eye to make her eyes look larger. Then we used a soft blush in diagonal patterns just to give a glow of good health to her cheeks. We finished her lips with a clear, medium tone lip color. We used blush up by the edge of her eyes to keep attention there. A touch of blush shortened the top of her forehead. See Fig. 80, 99A, 101 in Chapter 7.

JESSICA

HOLLY

Aquamarine
BlueGreen

Holly's arresting coloring goes ethereal in her right makeup colors. Her foundation supported her flawless complexion perfectly. Soft, we gave her eyes more intensity right at the lash line, then created a deep dewy look with gradients of medium to light eyeshadows. Her blush pattern close to the center of her cheeks kept her look of youth, and gave her a glow of health. We used lip liner and rich color to define her lips, a highlight lip color which contoured them increasing their curve. See Fig. 82, 99C, 100 in Chapter 7.

Ruby
RedPurple

Another dark beauty, our goal was to increase width in Haven's eye area to balance her narrow forehead with her wider cheek and jaw area. We added intensity and curve to her eyes with dark shadow on the inside and outside of her eyelids, lighter colors on the middle, then we directed her hair style slightly out in that area. A diagonal blush pattern broke the square line of her cheeks and jaw. We chose vibrant lip colors to bring focus to her pretty mouth. See Fig. 80, 86, 87, 99A, 100 in Chapter 7.

HAVEN

Ruby
RedPurple

Letia has good features. We gave her features more definition. This gave her a "finished" look. We intensified and elongated her eyes with dark smudged liner and an almond shape eyeshadow. The mother of Haven, we used a similar diagonal blush pattern to break the square line of her cheeks and jaw. We kept her blush pattern on the outside of her face to visually thin it. We contoured her lips with darker color to recess the outside edges and highlight lip color in the center to add fullness and interest there. See Fig. 80, 86, 99A, bottom lip in Fig. 103 in Chapter 7.

LETIA

Aquamarine
BlueGreen

Pert and pretty, in keeping with Jen's light, clear coloring, we used blends of pastels in her eyeshadows, her cheek color and her lipstick. To intensify her eyes, we used dark liner smudged at the lash, medium liner on the lid, darker liner in the lid crease. A diagonal blush pattern highlights the lovely apple effect on her cheeks. Jen has even features—easy to apply makeup and have her look good. We redefined her top lip with liner and clear bright lip color. See Fig. 80, top lip 101 in Chapter 7.

JEN

JESSICA

Sapphire
BluePurple

A darling gamin look all her own, she captures you with her big eyes and shy smile. Her hair style is a perfect complement to her look. We brought her eyes out with dark smudged eyeliner right at the last base then blended her eyeshadow pattern up and under her brows to intensify her pretty frontal bone structure. To give contour to her cheeks, we used a diagonal blush pattern that started high to bring attention to her eyes then moved your eye low so you notice the very pretty line where her lips meet. See Fig. 80, 93, 99A, 101-top lip in Chapter 7.

Ruby
RedPurple

Summer's penetrating large eyes capture your attention immediately. We intensified them even further with smudged dark liner and eyeshadow in an almond shaped pattern to make them appear larger. We focused her blush pattern up by her eyes as well as on the outside edge of her cheeks. We finished her lips with middle highlight color over muted rich color to contour her lips and leave attention on her eyes. Bangs reduce her forehead height. See Fig. 80, 86, 99C, 100 in Chapter 7.

SUMMER

JESSICA

Sapphire
BluePurple

An intelligent and inventive young woman, Jessica added cool brown nut colors to her hair which flipped her coloring into the browns of the current fashion. We kept her Blue Purple makeup colors because they looked more natural. This is a good example of how you can successfully swing with fashion but make it your own. We brought her eyeshadow out and down around the outside corner of

her eyes, contoured the outside of her cheeks and put blush on the outside of her neck to strengthen her jawline. Her bangs cut her forehead length and focus attention on her happy eyes. See Fig. 80, 91, 99C, top lip 101 in Chapter 7.

Ruby
RedPurple

Beautiful bone structure sets Rhonda apart. We used soft diagonal lines in her hair and makeup to counter the many round features in her face. We focused attention on her eyes with dark smudged liner right next to her lashes. We used darker eyeshadows on the outside and inside edge of her eye but stayed light in the middle. This gave curve to her frontal bone and lid. Her diagonal blush pattern gently chiseled the square lines in her cheekbone and jaw. We finished her lovely mouth with rich full lip color. See Fig. 80, 86, 99A, 100 in Chapter 7.

RHONDA

KRISTEN

Sapphire
BluePurple

Captivating eyes under high brows, Kristen also colored her hair but stayed in the cool blonde tones of the Blue Purple Collection. Blush at the top of her forehead shortened its visual height helping to keep your focus on her eyes as does the blush running high from the outside of her check bone in a diagonal pattern that created an attractive hollow contour to the side of her

cheeks. We kept her lip color simple, so it didn't compete with her eyes for attention. Notice the pretty line between her lips. We highlighted that with pearl lip color. See Fig. 80, 91, 99A, 101-102 in Chapter 7.

Ruby
RedPurple

Julia's face balances perfectly top to bottom; her features are symmetrical so all we had to do is further define and intensify them. We added depth and curve to her frontal bone by placing shadow patterned up and around on the outside and inside edge then we applied highlight shadow to the middle of her lid. The glow of blush moved from cheek across her forehead to the other cheek which formed a soft halo around her eyes. We finished her already pretty mouth with a blend of colors placed to contour her lips. See Fig. 80, 87, 100-101 in Chapter 7.

JULIA

SONJA

Ruby
RedPurple

Her open loveliness makes you feel happy just looking at her. Her eyes needed to be the focus of her face so we intensified and enlarged their look with dark eyeshadow patterns and smudged dark eyeliner that moved out and up following the line of her brows. A halo blush pattern shortened her forehead visually then moved to bring out the pretty apple effect of her cheeks. A rich muted plum lip color with highlight finished her lips and framed her pretty smile. We added blush on the outside of her neck to strengthen her jawline. See Fig. 82, 92, 99A, 101 in Chapter 7.

Aquamarine
BlueGreen

Kirsten has rare soft brown hair with her lovely Blue Green coloring. We featured her eyes with medium colors to keep her look natural. We then moved her eyeshadow pattern out from the edge of her eye to make her eyes look larger and fill in the space between her eyes and the outer edge of her face. We used a soft blush in diagonal patterns just to give a glow of good health to her cheeks. A clear, medium tone of lip color finished her lovely mouth. Here again we used blush up by the edge of her eyes to invite your attention to linger there.
See Fig. 80, 99A, 101-top lip in Chapter 7.

KRISTEN

ASHLEY

Garnet
RedOrange

I think of nutmeg, cinnamon, orchids, and far-away places when I look into Ashley's exotic eyes. We kept her brows light to frame her eyes without taking attention from them. Her shadow pattern, too, is lighter so we can more firmly focus you on her eyes with smudged dark eyeliner. She could wear several different eyeshadow patterns with the space she has between her eyes and brow. The diagonal blush pattern chisels her cheeks, keeps your attention near her eyes and leads you to her mouth with her pretty upturned lip line. See Fig. 80, 99A, 101-102 in Chapter 7.

Ruby
RedPurple

Inventive, creative, and daring enough to wear creative looks, Tabitha is a happy spirit. With lots of space between her eyes and her brows, we balanced her eyeshadow pattern with gradients moving from dark through medium to the highlight area. We added curve to her lid with lighter color in the middle section and darker colors on both the outside and inside edge. We kept her blush on the outside of her face in a diagonal line that countered her square jawline and brought you to her pretty smile. We also contoured her mouth to reduce its fullness. See Fig. 80, 87, 91, 99C, 103 in Chapter 7.

TABITHA

RACHEL

Ruby
RedPurple

Leaving her bangs behind and with a perfect forehead to wear her hair off her face, we moved the focus to Rachel's rich dark eyes. We gave them even more definition with a shadow pattern that moved around the outer edge of her eyes and beneath her bottom lashes. A diagonal blush pattern defined her cheekbone with more angularity while still giving emphasis to the soft apple of her cheek. We kept her lip color soft so focus remained on her eyes. See Fig 80, 86, 89, 99A, 102 in Chapter 7.

Aquamarine
BlueGreen

We wanted to capture and keep Carol's vivacious, friendly personality in her makeup. To frame and focus attention on her eyes and smile, we used blush to create a soft oval pattern on her forehead. We kept her brow color soft then intensified her eyes with smudged dark eyeliner right next to her lashes. By applying medium-dark shadow on the outer and softer brown shadow on the inner third of her lid with highlight shadow in the center, we contoured her eye lid. We kept her radiant glow with soft blush patterned on the outside of her cheeks, then used clear, bright lip color highlighted to add fullness to her lips. See Fig 80, 88, 99D, 100 in Chapter 7.

190

CAROL

TAMMY

Peridot
Yellow Green

A rare Yellow Green in coloring, Tammy's colors give vitality to her happy face. We contour her eye lids with medium brown shadows and intensified her eyes right at the lash line with smudged dark eyeliner. To give contour to her cheeks, we added blush to the outside edges then put added blush on the outside of her neck to strengthen her jawline. We finished her lips with clear, bright lip color highlighted to give a feeling of fullness to her bottom lip. See Fig. 80, 86, 99D, 101 in Chapter 7.

Ruby
RedPurple

Freda's beautiful face contours surfaced in gorgeous symmetry with well-executed makeup. The elegant arc of her brow was set apart with both a highlight and a dark shadow pattern that repeated that line. With shadow on the inside and outside and highlight in the middle, we gave curve to her lid, then lifted her cheek line up near her eyes as well. We finished her mouth, darker on the outside, lighter on the inside to focus only softly on her lovely smile—a pleasing look that still supports her intense eyes.
See Fig. 80, 86, 91, 99C, 103 in Chapter 7.

FREDA

Sapphire
BluePurple

A twin to Ashlee below, both girls have the lightest of blonde hair. Both striking beauties, Alicia carries a slightly bolder look. We groomed their brows to maintain their light look because we didn't want their brows to take attention from their brilliant blue eyes. We used an eyeshadow pattern to lift Alicia's left eye and a different pattern to bring her right eye level. Her naturally pretty cheek contour simply needed blush in a healthy glow pattern. We finished her lips in a clear bright color to feature her full radiant smile. See Fig. Left eye-81, Right eye-80, 99B, 100 in Chapter 7.

Sapphire
BluePurple

Ashlee, fun and friendly like her sister, looks gentle. We used eyeshadow patterns to just slightly lift Ashlee's eyes intensifying right next to her lashes with eyeliner smudged with darker shadow. We designed her blush to bring out the pretty apple effect of her cheeks. This brings your attention to her captivating chiseled bone structure. We then finished her lips in a light perfect pink to frame her inviting smile. These young women were a pleasure to work with. See Fig. 82, 86, 89, 90, 99B, top lip 101 in Chapter 7.

ASHLEE

Sapphire
BluePurple

Carrie's chiseled bone structure really set the stage for this remarkable makeover. We smoothed and evened her complexion with liquid foundation, shaped and softly defined her brows with soft brush-on-brow powder, then we intensified and defined her eyes with medium eyeshadow brought up and out on her frontal bone. We finished her eyes with dark smudged eyeliner. A straight across blush pattern shortened her cheek area. Two colors blended to give her a natural healthy glow. We finished her mouth with rich full color. See Fig. 83, 99D, 101 in Chapter 7.

CARRIE

Ruby
RedPurple

We wanted to focus on Caren's smiling eyes. To define and make them appear larger, we used medium shadow powder with dark, smudged eyeliner right at the edge of her lashes. Because her brows sit low over her deep set eyes, we had to be careful not to make either her brows or her eyelids too dark. We placed her blush high on the sides of her eyes to keep the focus there. Then we contoured her cheeks with a youthful pattern to give her a glow of health. A soft blend of rich pinks finished her lips to feature her captivating smile. See Fig. 80, 85, 90, 92, 99C, 101 in Chapter 7.

CAREN

With no **accurate system** to analyze hair color and **no accurate knowledge** of the color undertones in color formulas, **hair color** is a **guessing game.**

Getting Your Hair Color Right

Imagine that perfect color, the smashing effect that turns heads. Your professionals want to produce this for you. But often their stomachs churn—as does yours—because the guidelines for hair color are unsure. Having been a cosmetologist and salon owner, I understand this well. One stage performing hair stylist, Harry said, "Hairdressers are the most spiritual people I know. They are always in the back room praying, 'O Lord, please help me get this hair color right.'" It's so true because hair color is another guessing game.

But hair coloring no longer needs to be a guessing game because The Beauty Code™ and The Science of Personal Color™ System give you an accurate way of understanding your coloring and accurate knowledge of the color undertones in color formulas.

HAIR COLOR

Popular hair coloring products and tools used by professional hairdressers and salons

Hair color is a cosmetic. For a total look, you want hair color that harmonizes with your skin and eye color, just like your clothes and makeup. Your hair color can look natural, yet stunning, by using the hair color guidelines at the end of this chapter.

"The color theory that Marilyn Starr Harris formulated has been, in my opinion, one of the keys to success in the world of artistry, cosmetology, wardrobe, or for that matter, wherever color is involved. She has discovered rhyme and reason in a new dimension for the theory of color. As for my profession, the results have been phenomenal, exciting, and far reaching. She is a legend in her own right."
—Shelly Abegg, hair artistry

Your hair color will blend naturally with the "just right" colors of clothing and makeup for total harmony, head to toe. If you want to try a different hair color than your own natural color, The Beauty Code™ can help you successfully achieve not only a new look, but also fun and creative options.

To get hair colors you love, go to the beauty supply house or retail store and place the hair color samples, or the hair colors shown on the box, by the palettes of color in the Beauty Code Color Shopping Guide and Planner. You can tell quickly which ones work and which don't. I've put together several hair colors for each Personal Color Category that I know will work for you at the end of this chapter. I've also outlined how you use them as well. You can take these directions to your favorite hair colorist or use them yourself.

IMPORTANT FACTS OF HAIR COLORING

Coloring hair is a professional affair, not an amateur affair. Applying hair color without knowing how the chemicals in hair color affect the hair can create crisis. I know. I've had to solve many "home hair color" emergencies. Here are two important facts you may or may not know:

Fact 1: *The minute you apply peroxide in hair color to hair, it will turn the hair to orange or gold.* Hair contains a large portion of keratin which is by nature orange or gold. Peroxide interacts with keratin, leaving the hair itself more orange or gold. That's why people of "cool" coloring, blue green, blue purple and red purple, have problems getting hair colors that aren't "brassy." Brassy, in their case, means "too warm"–hair color with tones that are too yellow, gold, or orange. Their natural hair color contains blue. Blue is the most easily lost color in hair so it must be continually put back into colored hair. To get color they're happy with, people of "cool" coloring have to use blue temporary rinses, blue colored shampoos or other "fixes" to maintain cool hair color shades.

Fact 2: Hair lightens through stages. Brunette hair, for example, is the darkest hair color, and so it must go through all the stages of hair color to become light. The strongest primary color in brunette hair is red. Remove the black, you're left with red–which, in hair color, is not red but yellow-orange.

Hair Color is a professional affair

Natural shades of virgin hair lighten through these stages from dark to light: dark red brown, red brown, red, red orange, orange, orange gold, gold, pale gold, yellow, palest yellow, white yellow, and white. Please realize that the red in brunette hair is such a strong part of the coloring, it will never go to the lightest tones. This is why you so often see brunettes with yellow orange hair. However, this may be changing because recent advances in hair color in Japan show Japanese people with platinum hair.

To get beautiful hair color, you need hair color with natural undertones. My color charts show natural virgin hair along with notes identifying the natural undertones of each hair tone. Many commercial hair colors are made with the wrong undertones—again because up to this time, there has not been an accurate system to guide us in connecting color to people.

A male client, Neal, came to me deeply tanned with dark brunette hair and asked me to get his hair color right. When I asked him what his natural hair color was, he said, "Oh, I hated that. Don't start there," not telling me the answer. I covered his hair and did his color profile based on his skin tones. It was very clear to me that he was a natural light blonde. When I told him, he was shocked—I was exactly right. But he resisted mightily, since he didn't like himself as fair-haired. Patiently, I worked through the process with him, showing him how he would look with the right hair color in the right clothes. Colors in his shades of blue, periwinkle, and dark green really clicked with him.

It took a certain amount of faith as we stripped the dark color up through the carrot orange stages to get it back to a very light tone. Once he realized he had nothing to lose, he admitted, "I was on a hair color roller coaster. I'd spent months dyeing it different colors, trying to get one I liked: dark brown, orange, black, red, yellow, burgundy (that was the worst). Having to redo it every two weeks to cover up blonde roots was the most embarrassing thing."

His fiancée and friends were so pleased with the change in his look that he conceded, "When my hair color was finally my own, it brought my confidence back. I was able to be more myself. People treated me differently." He also said, "I wouldn't have bought a suit in the best color for me because I just didn't understand my color. But I love it!" Where shopping used to be an exercise in frustration, he now says, "It's great to explore all the different colors and color combinations that look good on me."

You are most beautiful
when you wear those colors that
balance you to pure light.

Marilyn Starr Harris

COOL COLORS

RUBY RED PURPLE	SAPPHIRE BLUE PURPLE	AQUAMARINE BLUE GREEN

Brunette

light

medium

dark

dark
(includes all ethnicities)

Brownette

light

medium

dark

Brunette

light

Blonde

light

medium

dark

Blonde

light

medium

dark

Strawberry Blonde

medium light

PERIDOT YELLOW GREEN	TOPAZ YELLOW ORANGE	GARNET RED ORANGE

Blonde

light

Blonde

medium

Brownette

light

Redhead

medium auburn

Redhead

light

Brownette

dark

dark

dark auburn

medium

Red

light auburn

Brunette

medium

dark

dark

Because your hair is so close to your face, it affects your complexion. Wrong hair color washes you out while the right hair color makes your skin look healthy and radiant.

This is why people stress over getting the "right" hair color. These and the following pages will help you understand how to choose your best hair colors.

HAIR COLOR FORMULAS

Wella

Red Purple	Blue Purple	Blue Green	Yellow Green	Yellow Orange	Red Orange
Platinum	Blonde	Blonde	Blonde	Blonde	Blonde (rare)
1001	1210	1290	1200T	841	892
1120	1120	1200	12NG-T	725	810
	1060	1180	1070		
Brunette	1030	1120	1036	Brownette	Brownette
5WV	1001	940		611 (N+YO)	729
507	882	911	831		643
336		811	711 (N +Y)	Brunette	633
367	Brownette			542	
237 + B	672	Brownette	Ginger	555	Brunette
148 + B	607	(rare)	9 WR	445	445
52	611	711	mix w/ 9G	257	435 + 356
51 – 1N	511				356
		Strawberry		Light Auburn	347 + 257
	Brunette	Blonde		8 GR	
T14	462	1036	T 11	6 RG	Dark Auburn
	411		T 27	6 GR	6R
		T 10			mix w/ 7NG
	T 18	T 28		T 27	

L'Oriel Preference

Red Purple	Blue Purple	Blue Green	Yellow Green	Yellow Orange	Red Orange
Platinum	Blonde	Blonde	Blonde	Blonde	Blonde (rare)
O1	10 WB	LB02	LB02	8 G	7
	LB01	9 ½ BB	9 ½ NB		
Brunette	10 WB	9	9 G	Brownette	Brownette
4A		8		6 ½ G	6R
4	Brownette	8 ½ A	Ginger	6 AM	6 AM + 4G
3B	9 ½ A		9GR	6	5 ½ AM
2B	9A	Brownette			
		[rare]		Brunette	Brunette
	Brunette			5 ½ AM	5 MB
	8A	Strawberry			4
	7 ½ A	Blonde		Light Auburn	4M
	7A	9GR Mix w/		6 R	4GM
	6A	9 1/2 BB		7 LA	
	6BB				Dark Auburn
	5A				4R
					RR04

Clairol Light 'n Easy

Red Purple	Blue Purple	Blue Green	Yellow Green	Yellow Orange	Red Orange
Platinum	Blonde	Blonde	Blonde	Blonde	Blonde (rare)
99	98	87	87	105 G	106 A
	99	98	102 G		112
Brunette	102	103B	104	Brownette	
118	103A	104	114A	116 A	Brownette
120	106A			114 A	118+
122		Brownette	Ginger	117	128
124	Brownette	[rare]	105G		
131	114	114		Brunette	Brunette
133	117D	116		120	117
	118A				129G
		Strawberry		Light Auburn	121
	Brunette	Blonde		108 R	120 +128
	124	87		106A	
					Dark Auburn
					110
					112 R

The difference between over-the-counter (OTC) hair color and salon color lies in the difference between an amateur and a professional. You can re-upholster your own furniture, fix your own car, make your own clothes, but a professional will do it better. Professionals work at their job every day increasing and fine tuning their skills. Because they work with many clients, they have a broad range of comparative experience from which to help people. They realize, study, and learn the necessary skills required to achieve a great end result.

PERMANENT HAIR COLOR Colorless in the bottle, the tiny, clear molecules create color when mixed with peroxide. Penetrating into the cortex of the hair, the molecules change chemically, swelling to permanently lock color into the hair.

Permanent hair color lightens the first 5-15 minutes, then after 20 minutes, it begins to deposit color. Tints cannot lighten tints or henna, so think lighter when you color hair. Roots lighten first so start hair color on the portion of hair that's already been colored then apply color on the new regrowth for the last 20 minutes.

Color levels 0-6 deposit color; the formulas contain more color pigments.

Color levels 7-12 lift but do not deposit color; they contain less color pigment so may need a toner to put back a pale wash of color on the hair.

TEMPORARY HAIR COLOR Large, colored molecules that stain the surface (cuticle) of the hair. For longer lasting color, apply to clean dry hair and heat with a dryer. Lasts two to three weeks. Gradually fades.

SEMI-PERMANENT HAIR COLOR Acts more like a stain. Small color molecules penetrate the cortex but since they don't change chemically, they gradually fade with continued shampooing. Lasts four to six weeks.

Our bodies are as intricate as snowflakes—*each beautiful and different from any other.*

DaVinci's Vitruvian Man

Da Vinci
and a
Code of Style

Y ou, as a human being, are distinct and different—a unique combination of body design: head, limbs, torso, hair, eyes, and features. As intricate as snowflakes, each human being is beautiful and different from any other.

This difference ought to be a celebration—a shout to the world of our own rarity, our own possibility. Our appearance creates the signature of who we are. Making this communication a purposeful and chosen one is The Beauty Code's reason for being.

The physical combinations that make up human body types—shapes, colors and sizes—are endless. Nearly all of them are functional and effective. But we are taught to value some aspects of our body design and to deplore others.

We are taught to compare our physical features to the features of other people. Years ago, I flipped through a beauty book in a book store that categorized women's bodies neatly into four shapes: H, O, A, X—meaning that some of us are shaped like a rectangular H, some like an O (all rounded), others like an A (with a thin top and blooming hips), and lucky others are shaped like the X of an hour glass.

If I asked you about your face shape, you tell me in terms of squares, triangles, rectangles, and circles because we are taught that. Depending on the time period and the current fashion, an oval face or the strong, bold square face is highly prized. At another romantic time period, women sigh for a broad forehead and pointed chin to give them the "heart-shape" look.

The human body is too complex, too diversified, and too individually beautiful to be defined by simplistic categories. Such oversimplifications are not only untrue and unrealistic, but they also promote unhealthy self-esteem. It can make us dislike ourselves and disregard our good points. Even when it is fairly benign, it misleads thousands of men and women into patterns of style that ultimately do them more harm than good because when the styles are wrong for their body type, they look imbalanced.

Here's an example to help you understand what I'm talking about. When bell-bottom pant legs were in fashion, our custom sewing shop hired a fabulous seamstress who was short, with short legs and wide hips. The flared legs in the pants made her hips look bigger because the wide flare repeated her hip width. When she abandoned the current fashion and started wearing straight legged pants with jackets, she looked taller and you didn't notice her hips. So, rather than trying to box ourselves into a restricted definition, we need the tools to express the uniqueness of ourselves in the best possible way.

The human body is too complex ... too diversified, and too individually beautiful to be defined by simplistic categories

Working with clients, I pondered daily about choosing flattering clothing styles and make-up patterns. We owned a fabric shop that also held our custom sewing department. At first, I followed the latest trends in clothing design and fabrics to help clients. However, experience soon taught me to rely on basic designs. I didn't need glitz; I needed good judgment. I needed real answers to create attractive looks and styles for my clients that worked with their figures.

One of the satisfactions of being an appearance consultant is giving my clients the tools to make the most of the physical and personality variety given them by nature and by their own nurture. Analyzing shape and size can be complex and finding workable answers requires a solid background in principles of art, design and science. Ever since the ancient Greeks, the ideal of feminine beauty in the Western world has been one of harmony, symmetry, and balance. Yet the infinite variety of our body's possibilities produces imbalance in all of us. Bringing these body relationships into balance assures your most attractive appearance.

Unfortunately, most of us cannot see ourselves accurately. Growing up in a family, watching a parade of "beautiful people" on television, seeing the physical aspects that other people admire, and forming mental images of personal beauty all condition us against seeing what's real and what's possible in ourselves.

With so many layers of conflicting messages, most of us need to re-learn how to see ourselves. Almost every client will point out what they see as their negative features, "Oh, I have a square jaw" or "a long nose" or "broad cheek bones" as if those features were a real problem. The reality is that, in the overall balance of their face, the features they single out are usually not a drawback. Often they actually give a distinguishing advantage to the face. A great example was a professional woman who worried about her "big" nose. After restyling her hair with more volume and interest and putting more definition on her eyes, cheeks and lips with her makeup, you didn't even notice her nose. I deliberately asked a classroom of people to comment on her face features to see if they would mention her nose. Not one person did.

Another example is that of a woman who had an irregular nose similar to Princess Diana. Dissatisfied, she had plastic surgery which significantly altered the shape of her nose. Princess Diana became a beauty icon and one of the world's most revered women without changing her nose. A trained consultant analyzes human geometry every time she or he sees a new face. They, therefore, have a level of discernment about the many subtle differences in the body. Most of us lack this discernment because we haven't had experience in seeing and analyzing a wide variety of figure types.

Rely on **basic designs** *that* **balance** *your figure*

Faces do not fall into simple patterns. The face, neck, and shoulders combine to create many combinations of wide and narrow sections. Balancing those sections directs us in choosing the many shapes possible in a hair style for any given client.

Quite simply, just as you would resent and resist any effort to dismiss the totality of your personality and character with a simple label, so you would want to resist messages that your body must fit a certain shape or mold. The Beauty Code™, as

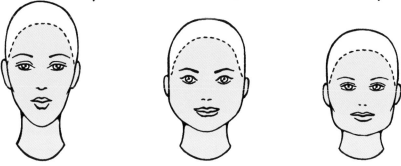

Figure 107

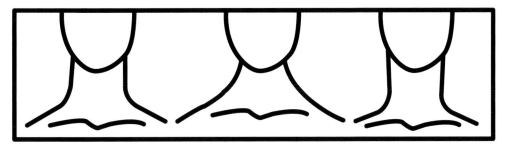

Figure 108

a scientific system of signature appearance, is a liberation from fashion "shoulds" and "oughts" that are not scientifically sound. It empowers you with correct principles of art and design.

Most of us have grown up comparing our physical features to those of other people–tall or short, fat or thin, etc. This type of comparison is not useful. What we need is to learn how to bring our own features into balance with each other to produce a feeling of harmony in our visual appearance.

*Use the **tools** of **clothes, makeup,** and **hairstyles** to **visually balance** your **features***

Figure 109

We can't cut off the ends of our shoulders, lengthen our necks or reshape our jawlines, but we can use the tools of clothes, makeup and hairstyles to visually balance these features and to control the impressions of others who are looking at us. Ideal style equals ideal balance.

Knowing your own measurements and features gives you a solid foundation to assess your strengths and weaknesses. Then you can balance your features with the right choice of makeup and hair patterns to create a beautiful, proportioned, balanced appearance every time. At the end of this chapter is a worksheet called Body Balance Worksheet. The simple act of measuring and recording your features will create a solid factual foundation for your clothing, hairstyle and accessory decisions.

This chapter teaches you principles for selecting clothing styles to bring your body proportions into better balance.

BODY DESIGN AND PROPORTION

I knew that the subtle interactions of clothing lines with physical proportions were an important part of the harmony and beauty I was studying. During my research, I was fascinated by the sketches of Leonardo da Vinci, showing the proportions of head to trunk and limbs. The ideal of Western beauty was inherited from the Greeks. The "Renaissance," the "rebirth," focused on rediscovering those principles of Greek classicism of the fifth century B.C. that had been forgotten during the Middle Ages. Not merely an abstract ideal, these classical principles had been drawn from a study of the human form by Greek artists and sculptors, both known and unknown.

Building on this knowledge, da Vinci had gone beyond their work, pushing both art and science to frontiers we have barely caught up with today through the sheer power of his intellect and the range of his incredible talent. His genius is recorded in art, sculpture, architecture, engineering, invention, and science.

Between 1490 and 1500, da Vinci focused his studies on the mathematical proportions of the human body. Nicomachus believed that "everything in Nature appears to have been systematically arranged by number, both in part and as a whole. This system of number gives order to the Universe." Newton agreed. He said that every element of our world can be reduced to a "mathematical way of reasoning." Color, sound, music, even our thoughts produce waves that can be measured and given a mathematical value.

Da Vinci measured every part of the human anatomy and compared its relationship to every other part, much as you have done (or will do) on your Body Balance Worksheet. As I followed his studies, I was astonished with his efforts. I am still in awe of his insights about the balance and proportion of the human body–the relationships between the various parts of the body. He made copious notes. In his notebooks, he defined these relationships with mathematical precision. For instance "the distance between the centers of the pupils of the eyes is 1/3 of the face." Or, "the space from the mouth to the bottom of the chin is the fourth part of the face and equal to the width of the mouth. . . . The greatest width of the face at the line of the eyes is equal to the distance from the roots of the hair in front to the parting of the lips."

I was fascinated as I considered the value of creating a look that worked to create the appearance of a body in proportion to itself. In the scores of books

*Nocomachus believed **"everything** in **nature** appears to have been systematically **arranged by number . . .** This **system** of numbers gives **order** to the **Universe."***

I had studied, I had never read one that addressed the complexities of this subject. Instead, they unanimously stated that if you are short, you dress one way; if you are tall, you dress another way; if average, still another. But I knew dozens of exceptions to these rules.

Take height, for example. There is more than one way to evaluate height: in inches, in comparison to others' height ("I'm taller than you"), or in proportion to your head-length. Da Vinci said the ideal proportion for adults of head-length to height is 1-to-8. Is this a universal measurement? Yes, it holds true for different races—both round-faced Chinese and long-headed Norwegians. Children, of course, have heads that are proportionately larger. Da Vinci himself noted that the head of a child is one-fourth his or her total height. Artists' "how-to" books show children at age four with heights that are about 5.5 head-lengths, at age eight, 6.5 head-lengths; and at twelve, 7 head-lengths.

Head-length-to-body-length proportion is not, of course, the only factor to be considered in clothing styles and lines. But self-comparative height explains why people of the same height may look taller or shorter than their measured height. The shorter the headlength, the taller the person appears in relation to herself. The longer the headlength, the shorter the person appears.

To show this principle in presentations, I've asked for six women, all 5'4", to come up out of the audience and stand before the group. Immediately, the group can see that some of these women look shorter than others. They also could spot the other figure imbalances. It was, and is, always a great visual learning experience.

One client who was 5'10" was upset when her computer style guide said she appeared shorter than her height in inches. She enjoyed being tall. Then she realized that her favorite clothes were those with lines designed to make a short woman look taller such as wearing beltless clothes in one color, shoulder to hem; basic overblouse with skirt/pants in one color worn with an open jacket. Meanwhile, her outfits with wide belts and outfits with light tops and dark skirts sat in her closet unworn.

Another client with a shoe size of 4 ½ was puzzled when her printout said she had long feet and could wear shoes with straps. She complained, "I have a hard time finding shoes small enough." But she was comparing her feet with those of other women. When she compared her foot size to her own body—which was very petite—she realized, that for her body size, her feet were long and were flattered by

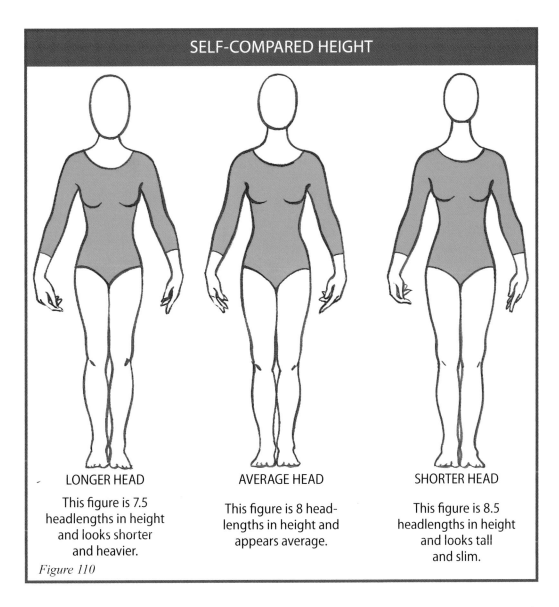

SELF-COMPARED HEIGHT

LONGER HEAD

This figure is 7.5 headlengths in height and looks shorter and heavier.

AVERAGE HEAD

This figure is 8 head-lengths in height and appears average.

SHORTER HEAD

This figure is 8.5 headlengths in height and looks tall and slim.

Figure 110

strap shoes which interrupted the eye traveling over her feet and made them look shorter. Suddenly she realized why strap shoes or shoes with horizontal designs were her favorites—the bulk of her shoe wardrobe. She now had a valuable tool of understanding to use when she shopped for shoes.

Self-comparative measurements are more helpful and relevant than group comparative measurements. Your arm length compared to someone else's arm length has no practical value. But knowing that your arm is long or short compared to your own figure helps you know how to adjust your sleeve length to achieve balance in your appearance. It also affects the type of jewelry you wear on your wrists.

*Knowing **your arm** is long or short **compared** to your **own figure** helps you **know** how to **adjust sleeve lengths** to achieve **balance***

This same principle applies to other measurements.

When I measure and analyze, I look for extremes in body, hair, or face structure. The viewing eye settles on extremes of beauty or unsightliness. If I can create for my client some areas of extreme beauty in color, line, or proportion, an observer's viewing eye settles there and not elsewhere.

The Beauty Code™ Figure Analysis and Style Guide is based on this concept of measuring body proportions. It offers more than eighteen billion possible combinations of physical features. That's a daunting figure when you think about choosing those necklines, shoes, hem lengths, collars, jackets, pants, sleeves, hairstyles, makeup patterns, and accessories to make you look ideally proportioned.

With your physical measurements and the computerized calculations, you become the expert on creating an attractive appearance for you. One client in Minnesota was delighted with the help she received from her measurements and style printout. "It's really amazing," she exclaimed. "It makes shopping a breeze. I don't take home mistakes any more. In fact, I don't even try on mistakes. I can look right on the hanger and see that it will or won't work for me."

BODY BALANCE

EYE TRAVEL: THE KEY TO BALANCING YOUR FIGURE
If we were to sketch you in black and white, this two-dimensional approach would recreate you and the lines of your clothing as a collection of lines and shapes. These clothing lines direct the path our eyes take when we look at each other.

Eyes travel from feature to feature. Even though we are seldom conscious of what is guiding or holding our eye, we all respond to principles of eye travel

The first principle of eye travel is to direct the eye away from anything unfavorable in your figure and towards your most attractive features. If you have short or broad areas in your figure, you will want to use lines or shapes which lengthen the appearance of those areas. Conversely, if you have long or thin areas of your body, you will want lines, shapes, or details that reduce the length and fill in the narrow areas for a more pleasing balance.

Vertical straight lines can slim and add height to the figure. Horizontal straight lines direct the eye across the figure and will appear to widen that area for a good

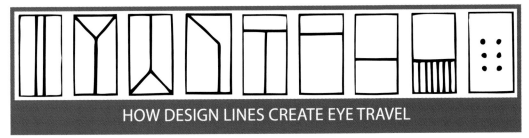

Figure 111

HOW DESIGN LINES CREATE EYE TRAVEL

The above drawings show you how lines direct eye travel to either slim or widen a figure.

or bad effect. Horizontal eye travel also occurs when shapes or details such as pockets or straps are placed on opposite sides of the figure. Even though the pockets are longer than they are wide, the eye travels back and forth between the two shapes, creating horizontal eye travel.

Straight lines that move diagonally across the figure from one shoulder to the opposite side (bust, waist, or hip) are very flattering, especially for heavy figures. However, when the eye travels down a sharp diagonal it will immediately look to the other side of the figure, seeking balance. In this case, the actual eye travel is diagonally down but then horizontally across the figure, side to side, just as if there were pockets or detail on both sides of the outfit.

Clothing that has been properly selected for your body type creates a feeling of harmony through its pleasing, balanced lines when you wear it. As others look at you, they will see the same pleasing balance and proportion. You feel this balance and enjoy wearing it.

I was visiting with a gentleman and his wife who were discussing a "new, perfectly good coat," that had hung unworn in his closet for several years. She expressed her frustration. Looking at him in the coat, I realized that even though the color was right, the double breasted buttons were too low; they cut his figure in the wrong place making his legs look too short and his torso too long. He sensed it and avoided wearing that coat even though neither he nor she understood why.

A high tie collar shortens and fills in a long thin neck; a U-shaped or V-neckline lengthens a short, wide neck. Contrasting colors within the body of an outfit shorten the torso; the same color in your clothes from shoulder to the hem lengthens the torso. A horizontal strap shoe shortens the foot: a pump lengthens it.

Because the eye travels from one point of interest to another, putting interest at the top (a fun scarf or collar) and bottom (shoe or hem detail) makes the eye move

Self comparative measurements are more helpful and relevant than group comparative measurements

quickly down the figure to make the person look taller. The same is true in helping you appear shorter. Place the interest at the middle of the figure, between bust and hip, and the eye will rest at the center of the figure, rather than moving up and down. This effect shortens the impression of height.

Details such as buttons on a bodice emphasize the bustline; center front buttons on a skirt emphasize the stomach.

Controlling eye travel is simply looking at each article of clothing, recognizing where the eye stops, noticing how the eye moves, and then using lines, clothing details and accessories to catch and control movements of the eye.

The second principle of eye travel is to break large plain areas into smaller areas. Break up broad hips with back and front hip pockets; large bust with a printed vest or jacket worn open over a plain blouse.

The third principle of eye travel is to cover the problem area. Cover the same broad hips and large bust with a long jacket, worn open. Wearing it open, divides the bust area into thirds which breaks up the space and covers the bust.

Because some of you do not have and may not get the Beauty Code™ Figure Analysis and Style Guide, I'm giving you some general guidelines to help you make more educated clothing choices, feature by feature.

Detailed styling in clothes and accessories is styling that shortens and widens the figure. It involves lines and ornamentation that move the eye in a horizontal direction across the figure. Detailed styling includes volume in fullness (such as gathers and pleats); volume in decorative effects such as cable stitching on sweaters, a chenille fabric jacket, fringe on a skirt. It includes accessories and noticeable designs.

Simple styling uses longer and thinner shapes to move the eye up and down, creating a taller and slimmer appearance. It keeps the major focus up near your face. It is the use of simple, straight or diagonal lines that run vertically so when others look at you their eyes will travel up and down.

Clothing, hairstyles, makeup patterns, and accessories give balance or imbalance to your structure. They should add width where the face or body is narrow or slim the wide face and body by reducing the width and adding the illusion of height.

Use **shapes** *and* **line** *in* **clothing, hair, makeup,** *and* **accessories** *to give* **balance** *or* **imbalance** *to your* **body**

The correctness of any look is found in the balance and proportion that the clothing and accessories give your appearance. My height is 7.35 head-lengths so I need to use every possible line to look taller and thinner. I use only two styles of skirts, straight and a slightly full or flared at the bottom. Any other styles make me look shorter and wider. Is this boring? No, because my body proportions look in balance, and I use color, quality, and variety in fabrics and accessories to give my outfits dash and spirit. I also remember past "creative" skirts that hung unused in my closet.

I love the freshness of new ideas, but I let fashion swing only after I adjust the tempo to my own tune. Once you understand how to work with the complexities of your figure, you'll find that it simplifies your clothing and accessory decisions. If you sew, a good pattern can reappear several times in different colors and fabrics to create different moods and meet different needs in your lifestyle.

"One benefit I love with The Beauty Code™ Color System is that it gives me so much confidence. Like today, I went into a coat store and walked through all the isles of coats. I knew in a matter of minutes whether the coats were in the right color and design that fit my color and style. I've saved hours in shopping and money by not making mistakes and having those mistakes hanging in my closet." – Mary Beth P, educator.

"I love the Beauty Code Color System for buying clothes. With the Beauty Code, I know how to be right. It isn't gimmicky. It works." – Rene B, administrative assistant.

Remember that you, not your wardrobe, are the art.

Remember **you,** *not your* **wardrobe,** *are the* **art**

BODY BALANCE WORKSHEET

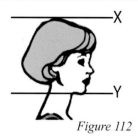

Figure 112

Step 1—Startup
Measure your head length with a friend by standing against a wall. Lay a ruler flat on top of your head. Mark the wall (X). Hold the ruler straight to beneath your chin. Mark the wall (Y). Measure X to Y. This is your Head Length. Now divide your total height by your head length.

The ideal body balance is two head lengths to each section. Less than two head lengths is a short section. More than two head lengths is a long section.

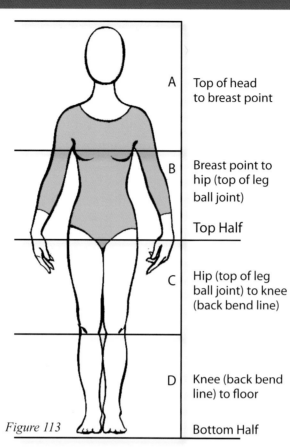

A — Top of head to breast point

B — Breast point to hip (top of leg ball joint)

Top Half

C — Hip (top of leg ball joint) to knee (back bend line)

D — Knee (back bend line) to floor

Bottom Half

Figure 113

Outside A+D

Inside B+C

Figure 114

IF YOU ARE:

Long (A) Head to Bust Short (B+C+D) Bust to Floor	Long (A+B) Head to Hip Short (C+D) Hip to Floor	Long (A+B+C) Head to Knee Short (D) Knee to Floor	Long (A+D) Outside Short (B+C) Inside
A Style Lines: Horizontal or diagonal style lines; interest, i.e. patterned fabrics, buttons, jewelry above the bustline.	**A+B Style Lines:** Horizontal or diagonal style lines; interest, i.e. patterned fabrics, buttons, jewelry inserts, ruffles, belts and waist interests.	**A+B+C Style Lines:** Horizontal or diagonal style lines; interest, i.e. patterned fabrics, buttons, jewelry, belts, insets, ruffles, pockets, peplums.	**A+D Style Lines:** Horizontal or diagonal style lines; interest, i.e. patterned fabrics, buttons, jewelry, shoe interest, including design and color.
B+C+D Style Lines: Simple, straight vertical lines from bust to floor including soft diagonal or straight skirt lines and plain fabrics. Interesting shoes draw the eye to your feet which lengthens B+C+D.	**C+D Style Lines:** Simple straight vertical lines from hips to floor including soft diagonal or straight skirt lines in plain fabrics. Interest at the toes of your shoes draws the eye to your feet which visually lengthens C+D.	**D Style Lines:** Simple straight vertical lines from knee to floor including short or long skirts/pants. Avoid skirts/pants that cut in the middle of your lower leg area. Wear plain shoes with heels.	**B+C Style Lines:** Simple straight vertical lines from bust to hips including simple bodice and no-interest waist lines in plain fabrics.

Short (A) Head to Bust
Long (B+C+D) Bust to Floor

A Style Lines:
Simple straight vertical
lines from shoulder to bust;
simple bodice and necklines,
i.e. jewel or V-necklines.

B+C+D Style Lines:
Horizontal or diagonal style
lines; interest in patterned
fabrics, pockets, insets, tiers,
boots, ruffles, varied skirt
lengths, flat heels.

Short (A+B) Head to Hip
Long (C+D) Hip to Floor

A+B Style Lines:
Simple straight vertical lines
from shoulder to hips, i.e.
simple bodices, jewel and
V-necklines,
and no-interest waist
lines in plain fabrics.

C+D Style Lines:
Horizontal or diagonal style
lines and interest; patterned
fabrics, pockets, layers, tiers,
boots, ruffles, varied skirt
lengths, flat heels.

Short (A+B+C) Head to Knee
Long (D) Knee to Floor

A+B+C Style Lines:
Simple straight vertical
lines from shoulder to knee;
simple bodices, jewel and
V-necklines, and no-interest
waist lines in plain fabrics.

D Style Lines:
Handkerchief skirts, boots,
ruffles, tier effects, varied
skirt lengths, flat heels,
interesting shoes.

Short (A+D) Outside
Long (B+C) Inside

A Style Lines:
Simple straight vertical
lines from shoulder to bust;
simple bodices, and neck-
lines, i.e. jewel or
V-necklines in plain fabrics.

B+C Style Lines:
Horizontal or diagonal style
lines; interest in
patterned fabrics, pockets,
insets, layers, tiers.

D Style Lines:
Handkerchief skirts, boots,
ruffles, tier effects, varied
skirt lengths, flat heels,
interesting shoes.

CHOOSING CLOTHES

Add A+B together to get your top half measurement.

_____
Top Half

Add C+D together to get your bottom half measurement

_____
Bottom Half

Compare your top measurement to your bottom measurement.

A. If your top half is shorter than your bottom half, follow the direction given for a short torso in the section above. You have long legs.

B. If your top half is longer than your bottom half, you have a long torso and short legs. Follow the directions given on page 218.

If both your top half and bottom half are equal, you're balanced. You can wear a variety of both vertical and horizontal style lines as long as you maintain your balance, top to bottom. Look at the drawings on pages 218-219. *Don't worry if you're normal and balanced. Enjoy!*

Notes: You can change your bust measurement by wearing a good uplift bra. This will change both your head to bust and bust to hip measurements.

Choose clothing to **balance** *your* **figure**

IF YOU ARE SHORT IN AREAS A, B, C, OR D

Use Simple Styling to Visually Lengthen You in Those Areas.

Use Vertical Style Lines

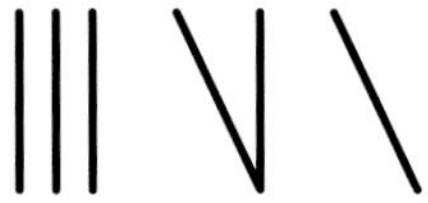

Simple straight vertical lines from shoulder to hips, i.e. simple bodices, jewel and V-necklines, and no-interest waist lines in plain fabrics.

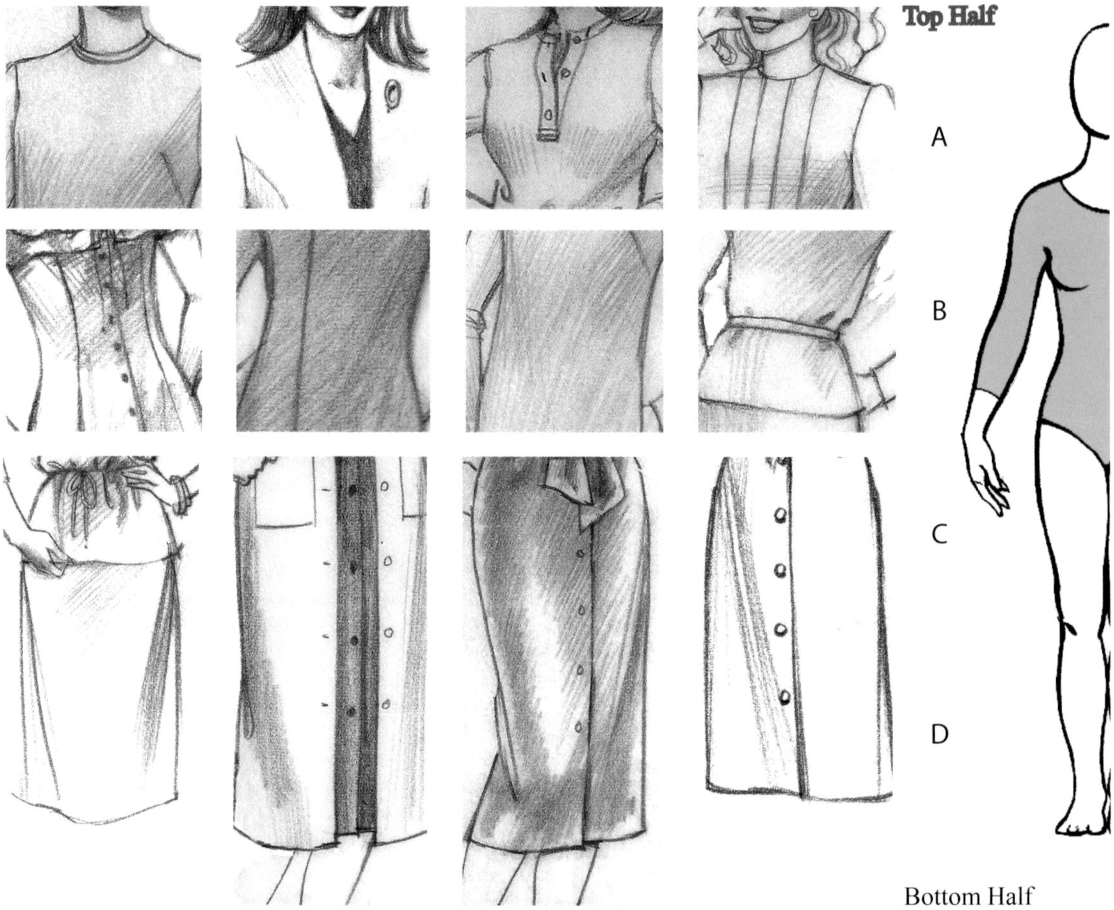
Top Half
A
B
C
D
Bottom Half

Figure 115

Make** your **appearance chosen** and **purposeful

I am:

A ______________________________

____

B ______________________________

____

C ______________________________

____

D ______________________________

Use Detailed Styling to Visually Shorten You in Those Areas.

Top Half

A

B

C

D

Bottom Half

Figure 116

Use Horizontal Style Lines

Horizontal or diagonal style lines and interest; patterned fabrics, pockets, layers, tiers, boots, ruffles, varied skirt lengths, flat heels.

My Best Clothing Choices Are:

A _____

_____

B _____

_____

C _____

_____

D _____

Relearn how you **see** *yourself*

To build a good wardrobe,
you must first have
knowledge . . .

Color Keys
to a Winning Wardrobe

To build a good wardrobe, you must first have knowledge. As you read all the way through this chapter, you will know how to use your best colors to build your wonderful, workable and fun wardrobe. Bottom line–if you always buy in your color collection, you'll have a wonderful wardrobe with a closet full of clothes you love.

Begin by writing down your activities in the three or four major areas of your life. Next, estimate how much time you devote to each area of work, homemaking, recreation, volunteer services, etc. Then, think through the kind of clothes required for each part of your lifestyle. If you're an insurance executive, you might need business suits for the office, dressy clothes for entertaining clients, sportswear for recreation. If you're a full time homemaker with small children, you know you will need more child-proof clothes than any other.

Why do you need a wardrobe plan? Because a plan eliminates impulse buying and buying clothes by impulse is like gambling. With no rules, sometimes you win, but more often you lose. You end up with closet dissonance and frequent frustration when you dress. What a waste of enjoyment, time, and money.

That's why it's so exciting to have a plan. By using forethought and your Planner Closet, your wardrobe plan becomes your shopping guide and directs your ready-to-wear buying. If you sew your clothes, you will be buying material and notions to fabricate your wardrobe. In either case, planning your clothing is part of being alive, and for most women, a pleasurable experience. Commit to it and you will find it works miracles in creating a closet full of clothes–with lots and lots to wear.

Your plan–simple, easy-to-use, one that works–will prevent waste. So organize yourself by taking an inventory of your clothes, accessories, and jewelry. What do you have that can be used or adapted? What should you give away?

chapter 11

When in doubt, put it in the giveaway pile, because it will just sit in your closet another five years if you don't. However, when I go into clients' closets and drawers, I've noticed they all hang on to old clothing in their right colors. If this is you, I suggest you have a "memories" box, trunk or other container in which to put these memorabilia. This allows you to both "keep" and "unclutter." Then, plan your needs. Be specific and rigorous about wardrobe choices in each area. Make your lists.

After you've separated your clothes into "keep" and "toss," wait for a few days, then go over your closet, your jewelry box, and your lists again. A three-way mirror is ideal to let you see what things really do for you. Be analytical. Wear a mask if you have to. Believe what it shows you. Most of us have constantly looked at someone else and never really know what we look like.

QUESTION YOUR CLOTHES

Once your closet is in order and your wardrobe list is made, it's time to shop. To begin, let me share with you some questions I ask myself when I buy clothes. Simple and straight forward, these questions test my buying decisions to help me stay with my plan. These can also help you sort through your closet. Ask yourself:

1. Do I need it?

2. Do I absolutely love it? Do I know I'll wear it until its threadbare?

3. Is the color right? Is the style right?

4. Do the details, texture and fabrics accurately express my personality?

5. Will it go with clothes I now have?

6. Will it serve my lifestyle needs on multiple occasions and several seasons?

7. Must I purchase other accessories for it?

8. Is it an enduring classic or a short-lived impulse purchase?

9. Does it appear cheap or of good quality?

10. Does it fit? Refer to the Fit Guide at the end of this chapter.

11. Is it worth the price? Can I afford it?

12. How do I take care of it?

The easiest way to build a fun wardrobe is to start with one color you love, either a basic like black, navy, brown, or a muted core color like:

Blue Green Muted Core Color	Blue Purple Muted Core Color	Red Purple Muted Core Color
Yellow Green Muted Core Color	Yellow Orange Muted Core Color	Red Orange Muted Core Color

Coordinate these neutralized colors with two to three of your best colors. Make yourself a planner closet: snips and pieces of fabric from seam allowances or extra areas of your clothing. Glue, tape, or staple these to cards inserted into a small photo or file holder to take with you shopping across town or across the world, because now you have your closet "in a planner."

Decide the clothing and accessories you need for your lifestyle. For my life style, day-to-day career is 80%. I have 8 to 10 pants and tops, 5 to 6 skirts, and 3 to 4 dresses. Professional clothing is 8%, dressy is 8%, casual is 4%.

Give yourself time—time to browse and consider clothing ideas, time to let the ideas filter in you mind and connect into your ultimate wardrobe choice. Go idea shopping. It's free. Leave your money at home and walk the mall, look and try.

Shopping is fun because you see so many creative ideas . . . some crazy ideas, true, but ideas can develop into new fresh looks. So enjoy the surprises. I love just looking at the interesting things designers come up with. Wait to buy until you find items that are just right for you, items you know you will wear.

You can also magazine shop. Flip through the magazine pages checking the details, hem lengths, shoulder widths, necklines, pant styles, hairstyles. Look at how the accessories are worn. Look at the advertisements as carefully as you look at the features.

I think of fashion features in magazines as the place where designers try out ideas of upcoming designs rather than clothes to wear. They are meant to stimulate your imagination and prepare you for the new fashions. To see what people are really wearing, I look at the advertisements. Tape the really great ideas in the Beauty Code™ Color Shopping Guide and Planner, inside your closet, or by your mirror. This becomes your Planner Closet.

I admire one lady who uses only twelve clothing pieces each season. She carries her basic pieces like skirts and pants forward from the year before and adds new colors/styles in blouses and accessories. She always looks terrific, simply terrific.

Impulse buying is like gambling.

*To **win**, buy your **best colors***

"The Beauty Code is a precious gift that people crave to have. Once a person really understands your program, they want to follow it for life. I don't trust anything else. I describe what The Beauty Code has the potential to do, my friends want it for themselves. I have always admired the fact that you put together this program by self study and out of a real concern for people." – Laura C., attorney

My clients tell me that, guided by their right colors, their right styles, and a wardrobe plan, they reduce shopping time and buying frustrations by 75%. Of more importance, their visual statements say the correct things about them. You will have the same capability, the same composure it gives them.

Match your clothing messages to the occasions to which you wear them. A fur coat has a completely different meaning in Alaska than in Miami. What messages are spoken with pearls? A turtle neck sweater? Leather pants? A satin shirt? Levis and a sweatshirt? Dirty sneakers? Hose versus bare legs with shoes? Painted toe nails with bare feet in dressy open-toed heels or casual sandals?

WARDROBE—THE BASICS

Because fashion changes so fast, the following wardrobe list is a guideline of classic clothes to give you a general idea of wardrobe needs and how to make better selections. The quantities listed are only a general guideline. You know your own activities and needs.

COAT

One basic is a full length coat, simple in line and details so that it can be used for all occasions in your life. For your coat to have an "outfit" look, choose a style that completely covers any clothing worn underneath, including fuller skirts and/or maternity wear if necessary.

Because this coat covers everything, you can choose a core color or another brighter, more striking color that creates its own total look. A skirt or dress in a coordinating color will greatly extend the use of this basic coat. One of my favorite full length coats was periwinkle. I loved it. People still mention seeing me in that coat—a fun memory.

Since it is the most expensive item in your wardrobe, choose a high quality fabric and fine workmanship. Check the sewing on the seams, buttons and button holes. Seams and hems should be wide enough to allow for mending if you should have to repair a tear.

Finally, test your coat for fit by stretching, sitting, bending, reaching. Look until you find one that fits well to begin with. Unless you've found an absolutely fabulous deal and are terribly clever in all sewing skills, never buy a coat and plan to alter it.

RUNABOUT COAT

Warm and sturdy for lots of use. Try for one that won't show the dirt and/or can be easily and inexpensively cleaned. Cleaning light leather coats can be as costly as the coat in some cases. The style and color should be neutral enough to relate with any clothing items that will be seen, such as slacks and skirts, i.e. tan, black, navy, gray, white, or other.

SUIT

Suits should be softly tailored, uncluttered, and capable of being worn for dress or sport occasions. The best fabrics are dull with self-covered buttons. This suit should be versatile enough to go anywhere at all hours of the day, even evening (with a long skirt) by using a variety of blouses, sweaters, vests, scarves, and jewelry. I suggest finding a great basic suit that can mix and match with different skirts or slacks. The best combination is a jacket, a skirt, and two slacks.

For your jacket, think dress-maker types rather than a man's tailored style. As women, our bodies don't fit the tailored style well. I think they're boring—especially when we could come up with so many more fun, inventive, and inspiring options.

DRESS

Choose two or three simple dresses in dark or neutralized colors with a very simple style that can be easily dressed-up or down with the use of accessories. See basic black dress below. It can be dressed "up" or "down" for either formal or informal occasions. These act as backbone pieces for those times you want to step in, zip up, and go with full confidence that you look great. Also have skirts and blouses that match and are interchangeable with other skirt/blouse combinations to double for dresses. These give more flexibility to a brief summer wardrobe. If needed, find one formal long dress that can be used for many special occasions and add variety by adding different jackets and jewelry.

"My confidence in choosing clothing and cosmetics changed after I purchased and began to use my Blue Purple Color Shopping Guide. I quit wasting money on clothing that was not right for me. I literally transformed into a better version of myself. Now everything in my closet coordinates together beautifully. I know I look good when I dress for the day. The Beauty Code has literally changed my life and my perception of myself!"
–Susan N., music educator

BLOUSES

Have two of each for dress, casual, and sports. Fabric and styles will depend on your lifestyle and body type. Choose a variety of colors.

SKIRTS

You will need three to five dress and/or casual skirts.

CASUAL OUTFIT

One-piece or two-piece separates for relaxed settings or sport events are very versatile. Be sure to *consider* weather extremes in planning your clothing, so you'll be as warm as necessary to enjoy your activities.

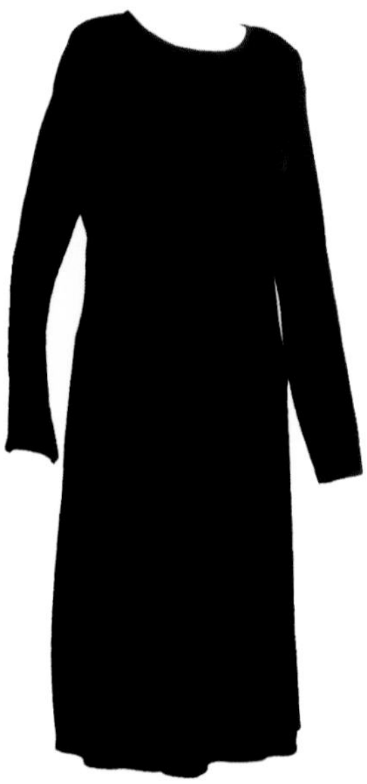

AFTER FIVE

"After-Five" clothing is usually more exposed for evenings. It can be a one-piece, like a basic dress, or matched separates. Make sure these are lovely in fabric, line, and color. Keep them simple so you can get different looks with accessory changes.

JEWELRY

Jewelry offers many different possible styles and looks.

I recommend that you acquire some pieces in each of the following categories:

- Simple: Metals in gold, silver, antique brass, or other metals for all-around wear.
- Sporty/Casual: A more casual look with wooden beads, enamels, scarves, leathers, chains, buttons, or other.
- Dressy: Pearls, rhinestones, other pure stones, ivory, or other for those special occasions.

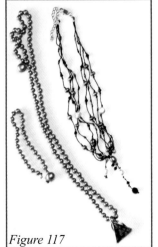

Figure 117

Figure 118

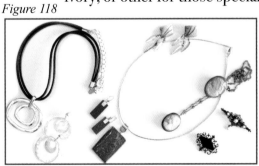

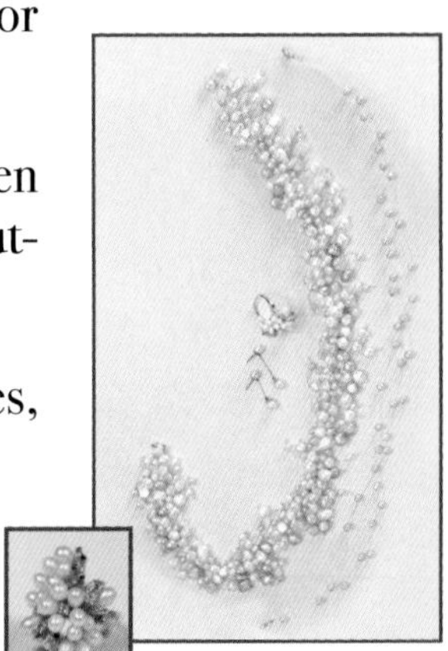

Figure 119

SHOES AND HANDBAGS

- Basic: Comfortable shoes for play and a basic bag for every day use. Include something fun for spring and summer.

- Casual: Matching or complimentary low heels and bag.

- Formal: Dressy shoes and jeweled bag for evening wear.

I'm busy and don't like changing bags so I have one—a good core-colored purse that can go everywhere, then I keep a small evening purse on hand when needed.

SLACKS

You'll need three to five in the same color as your basic suit for a pantsuit ensemble. Mix and match with different blouses for a dress-up style, a basic style, and a casual style.

FASHION—FUN AND FRAILTY

Today's 'must have' is tomorrow's 'hilarious.'

Figure 120

SWEATERS

Have at least one cardigan in a basic color and more for school wear.

JACKETS

Jackets are a terrific way to create many new looks with just a few basics in slacks, skirts and tops. I rely on a variety of jackets. Sometimes I roll up the sleeves of a career jacket to give it a sporty look to go with a t-shirt and jeans. Have one cold weather jacket.

HOSIERY

Have at least six pairs, including panty hose, ankle socks, and footlets.

ROBES

Have two to four easy-to slip-on morning coats, robes, or wraps.

UNDERGARMENTS

You'll need a minimum three, preferably five to seven, of each basic item, such as five to seven panties, three half-slips, three or more bras, one to two support garments. This way you have one on, one in the drawer, and one in the wash. It is useful to

have one full slip for two-piece dresses, two or more half-slips in colors that work with your other clothes, and three pairs of hose in the same tone.

CLOTHING PERSONALITIES

The fine tuning of your visual message takes place through your choice of fabrics, textures, jewelry, lines in bags, shoes, and other items. Your sense of yourself enables you to create this personalized style. Using your clothing with different expressions of personality, you can either heighten or play down the essence of your individuality. It is true that some people look similar or have similar personalities, but obviously never will two people be alike in both ways at once. Your individuality lies in your particular combination of color, shape, style, and personality.

CLASSICS

A wardrobe plan should be based on a strong foundation: classic articles of clothing. What makes a classic is its simple lines. These simple lines are attractive on a wide range of figures, they are seasonless, and they maintain a steady influence through the high and lows of each fashion look. Among the classics are the Chanel suit, A-line and shirtwaist dresses, trench coats, crew neck sweaters, straight or A-line skirts, the wrap robe, and the English tweed coat.

When new fashions emerge, if there is little you can wear well, take a simple classic style and add touches of current details and accessories like jewelry. A simple, classic suit can be sporty, dressy, or tailored by your choice of jacket, blouse and accessories. This allows you to swing with the fashion, and adjust it to your tune.

Classics adapt to each new fashion image, but the foundation remains the same. The pump might have a pointed toe and thin heel or a square toe and a stocky heel, but these are just versions of the basic pump.

While fashion cycles do revolve, they never really come back quite the same so don't try to keep everything. *Glamour Magazine* recommends that you save most wool sweaters, knee-length skirts, and belts, as well as items in excellent leathers, fabrics, or metals. Styles that won't return are most shoes, handbags, exaggerated collars, lapels, or cuffs.

The Beauty Code™ makes shopping a breeze. I don't take home mistakes anymore. In fact, I don't even try on mistakes. I can look right on the hanger and see if it will or won't work for me. I have fewer clothes now, but have more looks possible.   —Jessica

Because they follow the shape of the body closely, classics avoid extremes in lapel and shoulder widths, belts, ties, pant legs (straight, tight or flared), or skirt lengths. An acid test is, How will it look ten years from now? And how would it have looked ten years ago? The answers to these questions sort out fads from classic fashions. Good basic clothes last over the years attractively. For over fifteen years, I have saved two sweaters—one trendy and one classic. Both are styled so well, they continue to get compliments.

Some fabrics, too, are classics because they fit all seasons: natural cottons, wools, linens, and silks. Classic weaves are Harris tweed, Glen plaids, Scottish plaids, hounds tooth checks, herringbones, paisleys, polka dots, and tweeds. Natural fabrics, blended with synthetics such as polyester, nylon or rayon, can create a classic look but save you time on practical upkeep. Designer Donna Karan recommends that thirty percent of your wardrobe should be in seasonless fabrics and colors. Seasonless colors are navy, black, beige, white, red, purple, olive, cream, grays, periwinkle blue, teal, cocoa, tan, and taupe.

Classic shoes are the pump and the wedge in its several versions: closed heel and toe, open toe-sling back, or open back and toe. The penny loafer, and simple versions thereof, are a casual classic that serve you well.

TREND SETTERS

Some people are intuitive trend setters. They have the ability to take completely unrelated separates—skirts, jackets, blouses, pants, and vests—and turn them into interesting, inventive clothing. To be admired and enjoyed, they are a breath of spring air, the sparkle of creativity we all enjoy.

Regardless of whether you are classic or a trendsetter, dress for your age. Enjoy the beauty and experiences of each age, including appropriate clothing. Nothing is more distracting than a grandma trying to look twenty-eight by wearing hip hugger pants, halter tops or short shorts; or sweet sixteen trying to hurdle age twenty-eight with heavy makeup and stilted heels.

THREE YEAR ROTATING WARDROBE PLAN

Since most of us can't replace whole wardrobes each year (nor would we want to when we love the clothes we've gathered around us), I suggest you build a wardrobe plan that covers three years. You can purchase one expensive item or outfit each year, like a coat, suit or dress ensemble, or boots. This rotation makes a shopping list easy to organize. Good clothes can comfortably last years, so you may find your rotations expanding to five or six years.

Every year, fill in with less expensive items. Blouses, dresses, accessories, skirts, shoes, summer clothing. Just add a few new pieces each season. This gives perk to your wardrobe. Some women prefer having fewer and better clothes, and taking good care of them so they last. Other women like to buy inexpensive bargains and change them often.

Personally, I figure on shopping one day, every four to six months. Women who love to save money chart their calendars for the months when the better shops put their clothes on sale or shop at the many new discount stores available where you get quality clothes at exceptionally reasonable prices.

You can go your whole life going into department stores and being frustrated with the guess work. The Beauty Code™ enhances the beauty you always had but didn't know how to express. It helps you express yourself fully, outward and inward. It helps you to be more confident because you know you look your very best and you know how to do it for yourself. - Alexia

Buy your most expensive clothes for the major three seasons in your locality. In cool climates, long-wearing warm wools are comfortable fall, winter, and spring. An easy care, limited polycotton wardrobe serves nicely for summer. In warm climates, choose clothing for spring, summer and fall, adding a few warmer jackets, a raincoat, a few long-sleeved shirts, and pants for winter.

Don't assume that the most prestigious labels at the highest prices are the best clothes. That's a trap adolescents frequently fall into. Remember that the best clothes for you are the ones that fit your needs, your personality, and your body.

Sixteen well-selected pieces of clothing can make up to seventy-two outfits in combinations. That's as much as most people can manage to wear.

TRAVELING

Coordinate your travel clothes. If you travel a lot, always have ready clothing units coordinated to *three colors* of the *Beauty Code™ Color Collection*. One dark basic, one lighter, one bright. For example:

Red Orange	Brown, Tan, and Rust
Yellow Orange	Khaki, Tan, and Mustard
Yellow Green	Lichen, Banana, and Pimento
Red Purple	Black, White, and Orchid
Blue Purple	Navy, Mauve, and Wisteria
Blue Green	Brittany Blue, Cream, and Daffodil

This color trio concept allows for quick packing and more options, as well as more suitcase space.

A CAREER WARDROBE

If you are a professional woman, a tailored suit and a silk blouse carries the most authority and presence. A jacketed dress rates next highest. The jacket should be tailored or dressmaker—simple in line. A vest, worn open over a dress, is a fun option. The most attractive vests are unfitted, worn over blouses like a loose jacket. Fitted vests, difficult to wear for most people, look best worn under a jacket.

Choose solid colors, tweeds, small hounds tooth, Harris tweed, wool, cotton, silk, linen, and polyester blends of these fabrics.

Your best blouses will have long or three-quarters length sleeves and high, simple necklines. The fabrics should be silk or silk-like in white, off-white, pastels, rich reds, rusts, browns, or navy.

Your best skirts will be simple styles, either straight, A-line or petal skirts. Choose your best colors from among the basic colors in your collection: navy, taupe, gray, beige, camel, rich browns, or deep (very muted) fashion colors like rust, wine, or khaki. Dusty or muted colors can work as basics and set your wardrobe apart, such as dusk blue.

For shoes, choose basic or sling pumps or wedges. Hose should be in neutral colors and match your shoes and/or hems. For accessories, use simple jewelry of good quality in natural materials—gold, silver, pearls, ivory, jade, or wood.

Keep makeup and hair simple to style and easy to maintain.

Wear lined pants with a fully lined jacket that covers the derriere. In professional settings, avoid sleeveless clothes, low necklines, open toes, corduroy, elbow patches, denim, 100% polyester. Clean and modest never offend. Unkept and immodest sometime, somewhere will offend someone.

SHOPPING AND PLANNING TIPS
Now you're ready to spend money.

Because I know my best colors and styles, and because I also know which designers design for my body type and personality, it's easy for me to shop online and in catalogs. The benefits start with saving time and energy.

For store shopping, dress well and attractively. You not only feel better, you'll receive better treatment. Wear comfortable but attractive shoes. Carry a bag large enough to hold small purchases. Make sure you bring your checkbook with sufficient checks, identification, credit or debit cards, your shopping plan, items or swatches for matching colors and fabric, your Color Planner, perhaps a calculator, and measuring tape.

Choose the quiet hours of the day, such as 11 am to 3 pm. Enjoy yourself, but concentrate on what you're doing. If two similar items are very differently priced, compare the construction and fabrics of each.

One lady who has a very creative wardrobe remarked that she will only buy what she absolutely loves. This emotional response is good if it can fit into your individuality and plan. Don't try to be too systematic or you'll squelch your emotional responses and ignore your "favorite things."

Plan to spend good money on your basic tailored clothing, shoes, girdles, bras, belts, furs, gloves, perfumes, or hair pieces. All of these items get hard wear, and cheapness shows up fast. Trying to save here could hurt you. With careful selection and by shopping sales, you can economize on summer shoes, some jewelry, some hats, or purses, slips, and night wear.

*Plan so **every** item in **your** closet is **ready** to **put on** and **go***

In dealing with salespeople, be professional and friendly. You will save hours of time and frustration by telling the salesperson exactly what you are looking for. A good professional salesperson can be a good friend who keeps you posted on new merchandise and special sales. Some will hold a special item you really like when it is marked down.

If someone seems pushy, simply be knowledgeable and firm about your choices. Nearly always they will respect your decisions. Know how clothes should fit you and never, never be talked into the wrong size or color.

File your receipts in a small file box or book at home in case you have to return something. Sometimes it's fun to compare prices season by season and year by year.

SEWING

If you're an expert seamstress, you have many options. Sometimes you can find items on sale with great lines and colors that can be improved with a few modifications: change or add trim, replace ordinary buttons with distinctive ones, redo poor hemming, lower tight armholes, and add or remove shoulder pads.

One of my favorite wool suits was on sale for less than $100, down from its original $400 price. The skirt was pleated and looked terrible on me, but I loved the color and the jacket style. I recut the skirt into a more flattering straight style, then wore it for more than ten years. I always got compliments when I wore it. A good deal.

I always use top-quality fabrics because it's just as much work to sew on cheap fabrics as it is on good fabrics.

Sewing is also a boon if you seldom go to more than one or two formal occasions a year. Make a pretty floor-length dress that can be cut off later with the extra yardage going into a scarf or a blouse, or make a basic formal and change the look of it a little each year with new fabulous jewelry or creative jackets and tops.

USING SCARVES AS JACKETS

One scarf can give you several different looks, here is an example of two. The use of the scarf on the right actually looks like a jacket. You an wear a scarf over one shoulder and belt it at the waist.

WARDROBE GROOMING TIPS

Here are some valuable grooming tips.

1. Three right-hand helpers are the hair dresser, cleaners, and a seamstress.

2. Plan time each week for clothing care so that everything in your closet is ready to be put on and go. Unpressed suits, clothes with missing buttons, and unmended seams send unwanted messages. Take time to remove stains and mend, to wash and iron. Avoid overcrowding your closet and undoing all your pressing efforts. Special hangers and racks can help with this. Keep a good lint brush on hand, plus a cleaning fluid spot remover, and a bottle of clear nail polish to preserve costume jewelry or as a seal on the threading of buttons to keep them from breaking.

3. Keep your leather goods polished and clean so they don't show the wear. You can keep your purse cleaner longer on the inside if it has a dark lining and if you use wallets, and zippered cases for pens, beauty needs, etc.

4. Before you take clothing to the cleaners, empty the pockets and clip detachable items like belts to the article. Remove any particularly large buttons that might be lost in the cleaning process.

5. Have a "button jar" where everyone in the house places lost buttons, so that you don't have to replace a whole set if one is lost.

To conclude, the finishing touch to any wardrobe outfit is to stand up straight, speak with a positive tone in your voice, and smile often with your eyes as well as your lips. Positively anticipate your experiences. These are sure rules for being well received.

Evaluate the **fit** *of items* **you keep.**

Never *be talked into a* **wrong, unalterable size**

Never be talked into a wrong look

Evaluate the fit of each item you keep and never be talked into a wrong, unalterable size. Refuse to be persuaded into the wrong things. An ill-fitting garment is pure frustration. Develop the habit of testing all clothes for fit by stretching, sitting, bending, and reaching.

COLLARS

The neckline or collar should fit close without gaping or pulling.

SLEEVES

Shoulder seams should end on the top of the shoulder bone. Armholes should lie in a straight line from end of the shoulder bone to underarm, not bunch or gap and feel comfortable as you move your arm. Long sleeves should cover the wrist bone, and when you bend your arm the sleeve should come to the wrist.

BODICES

Bust line darts, if any, should end at the tip of the bust (Bust line darts come and go with fashion).

WAISTLINES

The waist should fit right at the waist, not above or below.

COATS AND JACKETS

Coats and jackets should fit smoothly over other clothing with the collar lying flat and smooth against the neck and chest. Coats should cover the skirt and/or the top of boots (This rule of covering skirts and/or the top of boots changes with different fashion cycles).

SKIRTS

Skirts should fit smoothly across the derriere and stomach with no bunching or strain. Waistbands should be firm enough to hold the skirt in place without pulling. Keep hems current with fashion but adjusted at the most flattering part of your leg. Pleats must hang straight and closed when standing. Side seams should lie straight up and down perpendicular to the floor.

SLACKS

Slacks must fit in the crotch area without hanging below the crotch nor pulling tightly in the seat area. Pockets should lie flat without pulling or gaping.

The exception, of course, is baggy pants, which are meant to hang loose. Cuff slacks and straight leg slacks should be parallel to the floor at the hem, not angled for high heels. However, they should be slightly angled for flats or cowboy boots. The front hem should just touch the top of the foot and hang straight with no break for women. Side seams should lie straight up and down perpendicular to the floor.

SHOES AND BOOTS

Allow room for your toes to lay flat. Crushed toes can cause painful and serious foot problems in later years. As you walk in them, be sure they don't pinch or slip anywhere.

WARDROBE OF NAIL POLISH COLORS

Choose the color of your nail polish according to your *Color Collection.* Each collection offers many possibilities. Here are the general guidelines:

Develop the **habit** *of* **testing all clothes** *for* **fit**

Plump hands: Medium to darker creme polish, matte (without shine) finish

Bony hands: Light or medium color, matte finish

Large hands: Medium color, matte finish

Small hands: Light or dark colors, according to preference, gloss finish

Red hands: Dark or medium dark color, matte finish

Tan hands: Brighter rose or orange tones, matte or glossy finish

White hands: Dark or medium color to make them look whiter, gloss finish; to make them look less white, use pastel tones, matt finish

"You buy clothes to make you look good. Clothes are an extension of who you are. So, it's a waste of money to buy clothes that don't look good on you. My suit, I would not want just any other color suit. And, if I hadn't come to you, Marilyn, I wouldn't have bought the right color." —Neal C., real estate.

CLOTHING MESSAGES OF SUCCESS AND FAILURE

Clothing communicates. When you have knowledge about the language of clothing, you can successfully communicate accurate messages about you.

SUCCESS MESSAGES

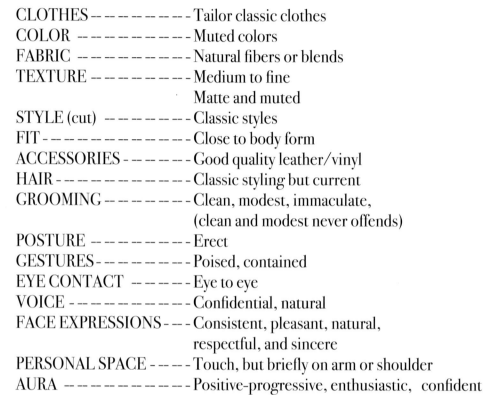

CLOTHES	Tailor classic clothes
COLOR	Muted colors
FABRIC	Natural fibers or blends
TEXTURE	Medium to fine
	Matte and muted
STYLE (cut)	Classic styles
FIT	Close to body form
ACCESSORIES	Good quality leather/vinyl
HAIR	Classic styling but current
GROOMING	Clean, modest, immaculate, (clean and modest never offends)
POSTURE	Erect
GESTURES	Poised, contained
EYE CONTACT	Eye to eye
VOICE	Confidential, natural
FACE EXPRESSIONS	Consistent, pleasant, natural, respectful, and sincere
PERSONAL SPACE	Touch, but briefly on arm or shoulder
AURA	Positive-progressive, enthusiastic, confident
WORDS	Good language skills

With the Beauty Code principles you declare appearance independence from:
- masculine styled suits with plain shirt blouses
- common colors and garish prints
- fashion that doesn't represent you

FAILURE MESSAGES

CLOTHES ------------- Trendy fad clothes
COLOR ------------- Bright, loud colors
FABRIC ------------- Cheap polyester
TEXTURE ------------- Extremes in rough and fine; coarse and shiny
STYLE (cut) ---------- Trend/fad styles
FIT ------------- Extremes in design
ACCESSORIES --------- Plastics, enamels
HAIR ------------- Outdated or trendy
GROOMING ---------- Sloppy, unkept, unclean, rumpled
POSTURE ---------- Rounded
GESTURES----------- Wide, loose, casual
EYE CONTACT -------- Averted eye
VOICE ------------- Whining, baby talk, morose
FACE EXPRESSIONS --- Extremes, bright, bored, angry, suggestive
PERSONAL SPACE ----- Too close or too distant
AURA ------------- Intimidating, depressed
WORDS ------------- Poor language skills

Many good books give you general appearance information, but if you don't know how it applies to you, it's useless.

Use *The Beauty Code*™ science to understand your differences and express your individuality in new and striking ways.

Merrie H
Topaz–YellowOrange

Depending on your age and stage in life
your body's coloring
will change in value—never in hue.

Color and Beauty
at Any Age

S helly looked attractive enough. But she didn't think she did. Her husband recognized this when they married. Wise, one day he started calling her "Beautiful." "Hi Beautiful," he'd greet her. "Beautiful, would you help me here?" he'd ask, or "Hey, Beautiful, what do you think about this?" Subtle, quiet, over the years, the message took hold. Recently attending a funeral of a friend, Shelly complimented the daughter of the deceased, saying, "You've grown into such a lovely young woman." The daughter replied, "That's a real compliment coming from you. You were always the standard of beauty in the neighborhood."

The same husband, wise or not—you can decide, told Shelly he wanted her to get up and put on her makeup before breakfast. When she asked why, he said, "The way you look without your makeup at breakfast, I would just as soon not eat." Ouch! Seeing her pain, he quickly recovered saying, "When you make yourself beautiful first thing in the morning, you seem happier all day. When you start working around the house without making yourself beautiful, you're always self-conscious—not as fun." Shelly accepted, and applied his observation as constructive criticism.

This brings to mind a quote from Frank Lloyd Wright, "The longer I live, the more beautiful life becomes. If you foolishly ignore beauty, you will soon find yourself without it. Your life will be impoverished. But if you invest in beauty, it will remain with you all the days of your life." The object of makeup is to look naturally beautiful. The object of looking good is to feel good.

"Women are the masterpiece of all of God's creation." This statement by one of my religious leaders reminds me that women are by nature beautiful. My experience with the young woman who cried in gratitude and revelation after her makeover saying, "I never thought I could be beautiful," reminds me that all women need to feel beautiful at every age.

Some get carried away with beauty and become vain. Some become foolish. Kahlil Gibran said, "Beauty is not in the face; Beauty is a light in the heart."

My work helps women know how to look naturally beautiful throughout their lifetime. It gives them the know-how to help other women look and feel beautiful as well. Part of my work is to forward the advice of my mother, "Beauty is as beauty does." I think of Princess Diana. Beautiful in form, yes. Then taking the unique challenges of her life to become beautiful in deed. Indeed. Totally beautiful.

Every woman deserves to look and feel beautiful. I hope every woman fulfills the opportunity to put beauty into her every contribution. What a beautiful world it would be.

When you ***make yourself*** *beautiful* ***first thing*** *in the* ***morning,*** *you are* ***happier*** *all day.*

FABULOUS GRANDMOTHERS: FIFTY PLUS

The entire world needs the influence of a wise and loving grandmother. By this time, you've been through enough fashion cycles that you've seen two or three repeats. At this writing, I'm aware of the third emergence of the bell-bottom or flared leg pant. My mother wore it in her twenties, I wore it in my late thirties and early forties and now my granddaughters are wearing it. And I still think their best look was the one I wore. I'm smiling when I say that. Just tell me we're not conditioned by fashion.

At this age, you appreciate clothes with elastic waistlines or at least some elastic in the waistline. Clothes a little more loose and comfortable, though more forgiving is the real word. Shoes that look smart and feel cozy to wear. Which reminds me . . . you know what really bugs me at this age? Designers think we're old! And they make old looking clothes. I hate that. You have to hunt forever to find clothes that don't look like something your grandmother wore. I know I'm a grandmother but, in our times, we still have so many opportunities to travel, to improve our talents, and to grow and learn. We're not ready to be old. We may slow down but we're not at a dead halt. So designers, please give us a break and design chic clothes.

On the other hand, give up competing with younger women by squeezing into tight jeans. We've had our day, let these younger women shine. Compliment them on their pretty figures and enjoy theirs with them.

Makeup after fifty is usually more subtle unless you're Cher. Not pastel, just more subtle. Glitter is gone; so is obvious shine. But you know what? At our age, if the spirit strikes you, you can glow. The reason glitter and shine must go when we're over fifty is that they draw attention. If you're very wrinkled, glitter and shine spotlight those wrinkles . . . on the cheeks, eyelids or around the mouth. But a soft glow looks healthy for the reason that softer, more muted colors benefit us more than bright or dark colors. Rich, that's a great word for us. Rich and subtle colors work wonders in makeup, clothes and jewelry.

Skin care—at this age, you appreciate (really appreciate) a good moisturizer and night cream that soften the wrinkles and tone your skin. Saggy and baggy—that's how many of us start to feel during this stage of age. If you're fortunate enough to have a facelift or two, rejoice. Caution here. Some women have five or six facelifts by the time they're in their late fifties. I prefer living a healthier life style and using good natural skin supporting products. You only have so much skin to stretch; we don't have to look very far to see examples of celebrities who have stretched their skin beyond the limit.

Hair color can be too dark, especially if your face shows many wrinkles. If you've always been dark, lighten up a little.

Diet and exercise take on a different meaning now. Those of us who flirted with exercise and diets in earlier years, now seriously study what "can be done" with what has fast become a serious "falling apart" and not only at the seams. I stay very close to my recommendations in *Diet of Light and Life*, a booklet I wrote about my philosophy of eating and staying healthy. And I take supplements because my digestion/assimilation "ain't what it used to be." With affordable home equipment and good TV programming, daily exercise can be doubly beneficial. My husband and I watch educational TV programs while we exercise.

On age, here's a quote I like very much even though the author's name who said it wasn't given, "People are like stained-glass windows. They sparkle and shine when the sun is out; but when the darkness sets in, their true beauty is most revealed when there is a light from within."

"I am seventy years old, I have been in interior design for over 30 years. Marilyn's color system is exactly on target. Color is an important part of the work my husband and I do. When I saw the Beauty Code System, I knew it was absolutely accurate. It is complete. It is perfect for finding your individual color. Most people choose colors that are in fashion, which is a mistake. If you're not in the current group, then you have a whole wardrobe that might fit you great, but you don't look great because the color is wrong. Marilyn focuses in on that. She shows you the colors you will like in your home.
—Marilyn T., interior design

THE REWARDING AGE: THIRTY-FIVE TO FIFTY

Totally
fully
create,
communicate,
and
enjoy
*new **moods***
and new
moments
in
your life

Why didn't someone tell me while I was in my forties and early fifties what an amazing time of life this is? You're old enough to have learned some wisdom and young enough that your body still functions with energy and vigor. You can accomplish so much during these years. It's that old hind sight idea again. But here, now, I'm telling YOU—now. If you're in that age range, make the most of it. Maximize it. Capitalize on it. Enjoy it. Make and keep some personal growth goals that will be exciting to you as you advance in time.

Develop some expertise.

Your family, if you have one, will move on into their own lives soon and you will want a life of your own. You need a life of your own. I see too many tragic women who stir up all kinds of chaos for their children and their children's families because they haven't prepared themselves to have a contributing skill beyond raising children. And even if that's your one and only skill, schools and hospitals always need volunteer women to help. I'm quoting Mary Englebreit here, "A life. Get one!"

Your hair. Your figure. Work to keep it or get it. You have now experienced enough success and lived through enough mistakes to know what works for you in many areas. You have confidence to change, to risk.

Clothes, makeup and hairstyles express you, beautify you. With my system, you can totally, fully create, communicate, define and enjoy new moods and moments in all areas of your life.

I'm a broken record when it comes to having a healthy diet because the older I get, the more reinforced I am because of the health giving benefits I feel. From my observations, healthy food is the magic bullet for health and beauty. I see women (and men) who struggle needlessly with every possible health problem from aching joints, killing arthritis, cancer, diabetes, and even just carrying extra weight. Sometimes when I hear their complaints and see their pain, I want to cry out, "Throw away the soda. Quit eating white bread and white pasta. Avoid white sugar and all the sweets it's in."

You can regain your health by choosing and using intelligent, life reinforcing foods. For you, who are younger, you can establish a healthier foundation for your bodies right now that will continue to benefit you right up to the day you take your last breath. As for exercise, do it! Make it a habit, even if it's just walking 20 minutes a day.

BECOMING INDIVIDUALS: TWENTY TO THIRTY FIVE

Just emerging from high school and perhaps college, you still carry the influence of the fads and fashions of your first impacting fashion cycle. You're rethinking fashion because you've moved into the second major fashion cycle (actually it's your third, but I'm not counting the fashion cycle from your birth to twelve years.)

Twenty to thirty-five is a time of life that we gather comparative information. So you try new things and make mistakes. You discover some things you just love. If you're lucky enough to have taken some fashion and interior decorating classes, you're ahead of the game. You're getting experience in who you really are and what you really like.

Usually these are the years of sacrifice when many of you learn to do a lot with a little. Young, newly married, struggling to get established in home and career, you're building your life's foundation.

Whatever **age** *you're* **in,** *make the* **best** *of it*

I remember a dear young woman in this age, a seminar attendee. Timid, she sat at the back of the classroom. It seemed she wanted to remain unnoticed. Her husband was in college so funds were limited. Her mother had paid for her to attend the seminar because her daughter "had such low self-esteem."

As the seminar progressed, I asked her questions hoping to draw her out. At one point, she got emotional, so I gently told her if she would come to the front of the room, we'd answer her appearance concerns. She felt ugly. I knew why.

She'd always had long, thick hair. She had allowed a recognized stylist to give her a new, very short haircut—a haircut that did not work at all well with her long, thin face and an equally long, thin neck and sloping shoulders. Her luxurious hair had filled in her face, neck and shoulders giving her balance and a pretty proportion.

I couldn't replace her hair. She had to wait out the long process of growing it again. But she could wear the right colors and choose some shirt and earring styles that could fill in around her neck and jawline. She searched for and found a five dollar golf polo, the ones with the collars. She wore the collar up and chose a simple pair of gold loop earrings. We styled her hair "out," away from her face so she did look, and therefore felt, better. Now she understood her structure. And you can bet she will never again let anyone—no matter who—give her a short haircut.

This is your time to try and explore different clothing. Having my *Beauty Code* principles will definitely take the stress and waste elements out of the process.

Learn to ***use*** *makeup and* ***clothes*** *to* ***express*** *what you* ***really*** *want expressed*

To get more comparative experience, when you go shopping try on bad styles at the same time you try on what you know will work. Notice the feelings you have. Learn to listen to your inner voice. Before I knew these principles, I remember having a dropped waist dress in a heavenly blue color. I adored the color but whenever I wore it, I'd instinctively touch the waistline with my fingers, an unconscious recognition that low waistlines weren't for me. When I wore it I felt like I had this long, long body with tiny pin legs running fast at the bottom. I know now that, with my structure balance, I need to lengthen, not shorten, my leg area, so I avoided dropped waists.

I also owned a chartreuse necklace and earrings, several bracelets, and choker necklaces that I kept in my jewelry box but never wore. When I understood my color and my structure, I gave them away—even to the right people. I loved knowing which people would love having them.

With these principles, you can create and enjoy the process to your heart's content in your own closet, when dressing your children, and decorating your home. I love seeing young women really get pleasure from knowing and using these principles. You can give gifts that others love. You can more intelligently recommend gifts, even for yourself.

FROM EIGHTEEN TO TWENTY-FIVE

At this time of your life, makeup *can* be bright, dramatic, fun, and even foolish.

Skin care? Start right now taking care of your skin, to build the valuable asset of good skin. Use natural botanical skin care products that are compatible with your skin. Read the section on skin care in Chapter 9, The Winning Look of Makeup. Achieve a makeup so natural, he'll never know. Go to www.miracell.com and learn about our botanical skin care line, MiraCell. Regenerative skin care retains your glow of youth. While it's not possible to entirely stop your skin from aging, safe skin care exists that is designed to slow down the aging process.

Because I had years of bad skin, I've worked diligently with

Richard Gadd to develop a truly natural skin care system that does support healthy, younger-looking skin. Made from the highest quality ingredients, our gentle formulas provide you with an effective, on-going health program to improve the functioning of your skin as well as its appearance. If you should have blemishes, use better skin care and definitely take a serious look at what you're eating.

Hair color is fun for you. You have several options in streaking, toning, or changing the color altogether. With the hormone changes that attend marriage and pregnancy, your hair naturally darkens so some of you have hair color quite a bit darker than when you were young. Many of you still want to keep that lighter, brighter tone. If so, do lighten your hair. Your younger skin with its healthy glow allows it.

Take a serious look at the quality of food you eat because it builds the quality of your body. Study some good books on both diet and exercise because you can build healthy habits to stay with and benefit you for the rest of your life. Food preferences are acquired tastes and can be changed. I'm going to repeat that for emphasis. Food preferences are acquired tastes and can be changed. This means you can learn what makes up a healthy diet and acquire the taste to eat that way.

I'm very serious about my recommendations in The Diet of Light and Life. Daily, I experience the truth of those principles and the healthy results of that truth. My husband thrived on milk and large curd cottage cheese. But recently, he couldn't breathe well and started having small tremors while he was sleeping. I realized he needed to drop dairy, so I bought several choices of soy and rice milk for him to try. He found a combination he likes, uses it and now if he goes back to dairy, he doesn't like the taste. He breathes well and the tremors have mostly disappeared.

Personally, I was so busy with our family that I didn't exercise and I still remained thin just by eating good foods. Exercise wasn't the big thing that it is today. But I wish now I'd built the habit because exercise builds a healthier body and it can be fun.

Take a serious look at the quality of the food you eat because it builds the quality of your body

"Wearing the right colors touches my psyche as nothing else. I believe color is part of the core essence of who we are. It defines our differences and unique characteristics. Color has vibration and frequency that tunes itself to our choices. My Beauty Code colors resonate with my soul. I feel a peaceful, inward connection that shows outwardly on my appearance. It's so easy with the Beauty Code education to trust my choices and decisions. Life just flows. No struggle to decide what to wear, how to decorate my home, or with other buying decisions.

"I've tried other systems but never found anything that works as good as this. It's easier to color analyze, give a client a natural makeup look, and color hair."

—*Georgia D., salon owner*

ACTIVE YOUNG WOMEN: TWELVE TO TWENTY

Making the transition from little girl to woman, you move from being validated at home to being validated by your peers, teachers, and any other associates you may encounter. You think the look of this time, your time, is the only way to look and you'll move heaven and earth to get it. And you know what? That's okay. It's part of your natural process. A caution however: fashion cycles and changing looks will be with you all your life. Life is so much more than either. Don't let fashion rule you. Take time to look at past fashions and know they will come again, with some adjustments for sure, but they will reappear in the future. This will give you better perspective. Keep some of your clothes from this time—you'll use them again for parties, reunions, and more.

I love the decision my granddaughter made. Moving into a new school, some of the leading girls decided to "diss" her by saying mean things about her appearance. At first, she was intimidated by it, but her wise mother got a copy of the book, Odd Girl Out, by Rachel Simmons. The two of them read it together. This plucky little gal decided she would wear whatever she wanted, when and how she wanted. A skillful seamstress, she designed and created original pieces that were well-styled. She still chooses from the current styles. That's usually all we have to choose from. She just puts things together in her own way. Sometimes she does something outrageous just to "throw it in their face." She refused to cower to stupid standards imposed by rude girls with shallow goals. She's much happier. All of us, at some time, have to stand up to situations like this. It might as well be early than late.

Decide *your life's* *values*

Looking back, this time is an important time for you to learn skills for future roles you will play. Beyond what you learn in school, think about deciding your

life's values. Where will you look to build your base of moral values? Will religion be part of your life? If so, how? What principles will you put in your life's foundation stones? Honesty? Dependability? Loyalty?

Do you plan to marry and have a family? If so, what relationship skills can you learn now to help you have better marriage and family relationships?

What skills and knowledge will you need in preparing meals to safeguard your health and the health of your loved ones?

Do you know how to earn, save, and budget money? Do you know how to prevent debt? Do you know effective ways of teaching these values to your children and working with your spouse?

What about maintaining a home in organizing, cleaning, decorating, landscaping, and fixing things?

What skills can you learn in each of these areas? Your education can begin right now, in your own home . . . even in your own room.

You can serve others less fortunate than you; you can learn first aid and about preventative or alternative medicine.

You can learn handiwork skills like quilting, knitting, crocheting, or history-keeping skills, like scrapbooking, photography, and writing.

Having some of these more important skills helps secure your own well-being, future relationships, and your happiness. Learning nutrition and how it affects our health is so important. Learn how to be a good cook. I've been in homes where the wife didn't know how to cook so husbands and children, day after day, ate cold cereal. Sad and greatly lacking in intelligence, care and concern for others.

FROM THIRTEEN TO NINETEEN

From thirteen to nineteen, you are learning and applying moral values like honesty—whether you will choose to cheat or not, lie or not, steal or not, be sexually active or not. If you take the time to look at the consequences of each of these decisions, you'll discover that often while the short-range results appear good, the long-range results can devastate. Good long-range choices always outweigh the short-range. Good morals generate responsible behaviors that reinforce you and benefit society. In these you learn to truly love yourself and become capable of loving others because you are integrating these values into who you are.

This gives you the ability to experience true intimacy in many areas, not just sexual intimacy.

Makeup enhancers compliment you. I'd use only what you absolutely need. If your skin is pretty and you have distinct features, you'll need very little. If you're pale with lifeless brows and lashes, you will look better and will be better received by giving more definition to your face. I didn't push makeup with our four daughters. I let them come to it on their own as they felt the need. Then I gave them good instruction so they would always look and feel pretty.

If girls are highly concerned about makeup, I try to refocus them on other values so they put makeup in a perspective balanced to their whole life. Then I show

From thirteen to nineteen, is your time to learn and apply moral values

them makeup to express what they really want expressed so they get results they really want. For example, do you really want to be seen as a loose and easy mark to be exploited? I don't think so, because the results of those relationships are not happy. And you want happy, right?

Experiment with hairstyles. My computer program The Beauty Code™ Figure Analysis and Style Guide can help you understand your structure so you won't let anyone make major mistakes with your hair, makeup, or clothing.

Keep yourself healthy with healthy eating habits. If you're firm in your confidence, you can set new standards of healthy eating with your friends. Salads can definitely be an "in" thing with your group. So can sports and exercise. But you're of the gym enthusiast generation, so this may be old hat to you.

THANK HEAVEN FOR LITTLE GIRLS: BIRTH TO TWELVE

I'm very tender about little girls . . . and little boys, too. So much of what we do affects them. Precious is the first word that comes to my mind. Sure, they have to learn to discipline themselves and they can learn with quiet, firm directions and good follow through. I just want them to have their time of innocence, to have the full flavor and experience natural to each stage from birth to twenty.

Marilyn Monroe, an actress from the 50's with tragic life consequences, said, "No one ever told me I was pretty when I was a little girl. All little girls should be told they're pretty, even if they aren't."

*Every woman **deserves** to **look** and **feel** beautiful.*

*I hope **every woman** fulfills the opportunity to put **beauty** into her **every** contribution.*

The following are quick examples of the tasks of each period of growth. For example, from birth to eighteen months little girls form their feelings of security by having dependable, loving attachments. The essence of this mode is that they are given this security in a loving home; they develop the ability to reach out.

From eighteen months to three years, they learn about their world by exploring it, hence the term "terrible twos" because they're into everything as they explore to understand "difference." Three to four years old, I call the magical years because they are getting a sense of themselves and their identity through their imagination. Little girls pretend they are the heroines from whatever they're exposed to—Disney, *Little Women, Heidi.* Little boys, in the same way, imagine themselves the hero. Just learning to express themselves, it's a delight to eavesdrop into their adventures.

Clothes should be fun and comfortable, allowing them to play with freedom. Our daughter, Sara put reachable shelves in her daughter's closet along with stacks of pants and shirts where Shelby can reach them to choose her own clothes. Or you can pre-bundle them. Shelby chooses to wear her best colors instinctively.

I love Shelby's other grandmother, Carolyn, who always buys Shelby imaginative clothes with sparkles, ruffles, and frills. Her mother, Sara, won a trip for the family on the Disney boat and I got to tag along to help tend their twins. Recognizing Shelby was in the imaginative age and wanting to reinforce her sense of being, I bought her a Belle outfit (from Disney's *Beauty and the Beast*) to wear to the evening meals. In her mind, she was Belle. She walked, talked, and moved her hands just as she imagined Belle would.

From four to seven, children start to do those things that develop their competence. Reading, writing, arithmetic, yes. Also, they learn how to ride a bike, roller blade, bathe themselves, take care of their clothes and their rooms, and perhaps start dance or karate lessons. All of these give them a sense of their own personal power to make things happen, to achieve. Through this they experience the thrill of winning, the pain of losing, and the realities of competition.

Having developed some degree of competence by seven, they begin to look beyond themselves and their homes from seven to thirteen. They learn care and concern for others, they share pain in seeing someone get hurt or suffer loss. They sympathize and empathize.

Because childhood is so precious to me, I don't like seeing little girls perform dances or dress with sexual overtones. Allow innocence to reign for these brief few, formative years. Let makeup be for play or performance, for imagination not stimulation.

Hair, like clothes, can be simple for daily school or play; fanciful for special events.

As to diet, even little girls can learn that some foods are better for them than others. I realized that every year after Halloween, our children got colds.

As I studied, I learned that white sugar depletes our calcium and vitamin C, leaving us open to germs that cause sickness. So my husband and I would bargain with them for their extra candy with cold hard cash. We'd let them enjoy the first rush of their "treats from tricking" but quickly had them back on a healthy diet. Honestly, during our children's' growing up years, I'd just fill our table with fresh

Little girls **form** *their* **feelings** *of security by having* **dependable, loving** *attachments*

fruits and vegetables including sprouts, whole grain bread, and cereal and milk. We didn't have a runny nose at home for four years and we had five children under eight years old. That's really remarkable when you think about it.

Each stage, each age of life gives amazing gifts of wonder and being

Each stage, each age of life amazes me with its wonder and gifts of being. I love this quote of Ashley Smith, "Life is full of beauty. Notice it. Notice the bumble bee, the small child, and the smiling faces. Smell the rain, and feel the wind. Live your life into the fullest potential and fight for your dreams."

I've experienced some really tough things in my life; things I never thought I'd have to deal with. But you know what? I did and I have. I can honestly say I'm grateful because each harsh experience has taught me greater understanding, wisdom and compassion. These awesome gifts enrich my character.

Love your life. Love and honor yourself each day as you experience what that day has to bring to you. Live your life with integrity to what you, in your deepest heart, believe to be true. Continue to grow and do better. You'll have peace, confidence, and an inner resourcefulness that belongs fully, wholly to you. Go forward with my love and my faith in you.

Love your life

Love and honor yourself

In his 1994 inaugural speech, Nelson Mandela said, "We ask ourselves, 'Who am I to be brilliant, gorgeous, talented, and famous?' Actually, who are you not to be? You are a child of God. Your playing small does not serve the world. There is nothing enlightened about shrinking so that people won't feel insecure around you. We were born to make manifest the glory of God that is within us. It's not just in some of us; it's in all of us. And when we let our own light shine, we unconsciously give other people permission to do the same. As we are liberated from our own fear, our presence automatically liberates others."

Maybe that's what John Keats meant when he said, "Beauty is truth, truth beauty— that is all ye know on earth, and all ye need to know."

BEAUTY is Truth

TRUTH is Beauty

Look
at your
results.

The Wellspring of Beauty

"The perception of color—including feeling and emotion—is the property of human consciousness. If man is awed by what he sees in his surroundings, he should be far more impressed by what lies within the sanctuary of his own being. This is where to look, not in ignorance, but in sensitive understanding."

Author Unknown

Beauty or ugliness is created in man's environment because it was first created in a woman's or man's brain. The Impressionists found laws in nature and combined them with the genius in their own minds to give us beauty that has surpassed the ages. Dr. Robert Schluter reminds us, "The colors used by Leonardo da Vinci in his *Mona Lisa* are still studied by art scholars."

Much of my professional life has been dedicated to helping people define their appearance. It's rewarding to help people—to see them improve themselves through better understanding of themselves. The underlying objective of The Beauty Code™ is to help people discover and reveal the light in themselves and to see the positive effects of that light in those around us.

I am fortunate. This work has placed me in a position to see these changes in people. Seeing those changes never ceases to impress me with how physical appearance affects attitude. In turn, improved attitude consistently and positively impacts other areas of the person's life.

Appearance contributes to that personal signature with which we face the society in which we live, move, and have being. More than outward visuals and other's perfections, more than a statement of style, our appearance indicates our well-being. It helps us define ourselves to know who we are.

THE POWER OF BEAUTY

Because my parents placed limited importance on personal appearance, I often felt unsure about the relevance of working in the field of beauty. This changed for me when a timid young woman entered my makeup studio for consultation on her makeup and hairstyle.

It seemed to be a normal appointment. I completed her color analysis, shampooed and styled her hair, assisted her with her make-up and was putting her color palette on her so she could see the total effect. She became very quiet. Seeing the finished result, tears began running down her cheeks. Confused, I asked her, "Is anything wrong?"

"No," was her stammered, embarrassed reply. "It's just that I never thought I could be beautiful."

For the first time in her life she saw an image of herself that greatly expanded her view of who she was and could be. An intelligent young woman, her personal self-image didn't match with her possibility. At that moment, I realized that by giving people the visual representation of their potential, I was giving them something much more—a greater awareness of who they were within. I felt happy, fulfilled. In order to accurately reflect our clients, it became even more important to have correct analysis and guidance materials.

Even then, some clients have such a poor self-image they won't believe they are attractive and end up bringing their appearance down to the level of their self belief. How sad. How often does the personal destruction of beauty begin, continue, and end with our own thinking?

The Beauty Code™ exists to assist each person in creating a personal signature of self that is both a statement and an achievement, a statement of who they are, an achievement of the power in themselves. When the innate powers of a person are brought into balance, the result is the same as balancing the effects of the prism—pure light. The Beauty Code™ is committed to the prism of self and to providing self-knowledge and personal power through information and education.

So while The Beauty Code™ is makeup, color, wardrobe, and fashion, it is also attitude, character, and integrity. The Beauty Code™ allows you to put appearance in perspective and move forward with confidence. How exciting for us to use our time, energy, and potential in discovering our wholeness and creating our

Physical **appearance** **affects** *your* **attitude**

Improved attitude **impacts** *other areas of* **your life**

own possibility—our own contribution.

THE POWER OF SELF-PERCEPTION

The journey of self-discovery begins with how we think about ourselves. Our thoughts are as tangible and measurable as radio waves. Because thoughts are matter, they do matter. Our thoughts about ourselves create who we are.

It's good to feel good. Feeling beautiful is a wholesome emotion. Looking beautiful is a declaration of self, a celebration. Personal beauty is created as you progress from concept to conclusion. Concepts are the ways in which you think about yourselves, the values that are intrinsically important to you. Conclusions are the manner in which you dress to express your self-concepts, the contributions you make that give meaning to yourself and others.

For a sense of completeness, there must be a liaison between your personal character, your feelings, and your personal appearance. Like interlocking triangles, that association will become a total integration, leaving you in control. Ultimately, the control of self must be governed by correct principles.

CORRECT PRINCIPLES ARE POWER

Correct principles will take us where we want to go. To be truly successful, the mind uses correct principles to direct both feelings and actions. Consider this Success Equation.

RIGHT PRINCIPLES + RIGHT ACTION = POSITIVE RESULTS

You are intelligence, emotion, and material. You think, feel and act. You have a mind, a spirit, and a body. Too often, too much, the view is that you are only physical entities—a body to wear this dress, buy that car, or use these helpful household articles. But you are much more than that.

The material body needs the direction of the intelligent mind. The mind needs correct principles to steer its direction. If the body becomes overbearing in its demands, the mind is never heard. If the body's passions are allowed to take control, physical drives like eating, sex, money, and status become the governing force, wisdom, and reason become secondary to the gratification of physical appetite. The more we allow our passions to gain control, the weaker our wisdom becomes.

*For a **sense** of **completeness**, you must **align** your **inner** and **outer perception** of **yourself***

Emotions too, can control us if we let them. We can become obsessed with worry, jealousy, and blaming. Our mind, using right principles, can choose our emotions. For example, if I choose to live by the principles of encouragement, then I can choose and apply the emotion of faith and belief in my relationships. This leads me to compliment and encourage those close to me rather than criticize them because I have faith in them to figure things out. When negative emotion rules, expressions of anger or revenge wantonly destroy and disrupt; even positive emotions like sympathy and sweetness in excess can enable others destructively.

To choose ***good*** *for yourself* ***look*** *at the* ***results*** *that come from* ***your*** ***principles***

You can choose. I can choose–the channels we want our lives to play on. How we handle our physical drives and emotions is a choice, a process of our mind, our *will*. A person must "will" that principles will rule over emotions and appetites, that we can make decisions and govern our thoughts and actions without letting emotions rule. Will, the power of conscious deliberate action, comes from that part of you that will never change, your core intelligence.

Our emotions are not the real us. They can be painfully misleading and at best we have imperfect control over them. It is through "willing" to live by principle that our choices will lead us to the happiness we seek.

The role of religion is to give us directing principles of eternal value. Psychiatry helps us understand our emotions and how they affect our actions. For physical understanding we have myriads of nutrition, diet, exercise, and appearance books–and magazines and programs. Help through understanding beckons all around us.

HAPPINESS IS SUCCESS

In my presentations, I make it a practice to ask people three simple questions:

1. Do you want to be happy or unhappy?
2. Do you want to be attractive or plain and passed over?
3. Do you want to be successful or unsuccessful?

Invariably the responses are alike. Everyone wants to be happy. We all wish to be seen as attractive. And success in its many forms is appealing. Given that this is true, why then are there so many unhappy and unsuccessful people who feel unattractive?

Why? They don't know how to make success happen. They lack the correct principles that direct their behaviors and emotions in paths that lead to happiness. These can be learned. Just as you can learn the skills of outer appearance, you can learn good principles that govern and build confidence and happiness through capability.

Socrates taught this with finesse. He said that goodness is based on knowledge and wickedness on ignorance. No wise man would choose what is bad for him in the long run. But most men, through ignorance, would choose the evil that looks good at the time.

As a fabric buyer, I purchased from many companies. I soon learned who I could and couldn't trust. I regularly ordered exact amounts for weddings or custom sewing orders. One company consistently shorted me one to three yards on my orders. They lost my business. Trusted companies earned double and triple my business.

To choose good for yourself, look at the results that you are getting from your principles. False principles produce unsatisfactory results—unhappiness, failure, and misery; correct principles produce satisfying results—happiness, fulfillment, and peace.

The results of living by the principle of honesty are that people trust you, they know where you stand and what to expect from you, and you have more freedom and opportunity in your associations. You may add to honesty the skill of diplomacy so you're not abrasive. On the other hand, because of dishonesty, many individuals and businesses have lost not only opportunities, but also fortunes because people would no longer deal with them.

The result of living by the principle of honesty is that people trust you

The principle of respect for others teaches us that we cannot tread over others and expect to enjoy in full measure the reward of our own success. Principles of knowledge, order, morality and integrity remain constant while still leaving us free to express individuality in the vast free space of life. This makes life a constant wonder in facing new experience with the confidence that we can meet the challenges.

We learn from the law of cause and effect that a universal law exists behind all life, impersonally rewarding us or hurting us according to the principles by which we choose to direct ourselves.

Which principles would you like to direct your life? You can think about it and choose. We act on what we believe to be true. Our results come from on what really is true.

If you don't like where or what you are right now, then look at the principles that you live by. A change may be in order. Look for different principles that evoke different attitudes and beliefs to direct different behaviors.

BEING BEAUTIFUL: COMPLETING CONFIDENCE

As I work to help my clients make appearance decisions, it has been my experience that many women struggle for confidence. To anyone daily fighting a battle to determine their identity, understand that your rights for equality are won. What you need is the inner connection that takes you from where you are to where you want to be.

The conflict that must be resolved is an internal one. The power to create your own existence is your choice. It is only within yourself that you find the determination to use the qualities of your own beauty, the clarity of your own vision, and the sense of your values. Your personal power to achieve and create gains integrity as you live by what you sense within to be truth.

The power to **create** *your* **own** **experience** *is your* **choice**

Assessing who you are and what you wish to become is the first step in achieving personal freedom. This is your plan. External forces cannot manipulate or control you unless you grant them that ability. Your contribution to society is valuable. It's time to end your confusion and begin your contribution. Sir Robert Baden-Powell said: "When you remove the masks [and] take away the defenses, guilts, doubts, and inhibitions, you find a beautiful person waiting to experience life emotionally, spiritually, and creatively."

Stop and think, write and consider. What do you love? What is infinitely important to you? What kind of a person do you want to be today? Tomorrow? At the end of your life?

A very attractive young woman sat slumped over in my class with her head down and her arms folded protectively across her chest. Recognizing poor posture as a sign of poor self-image, I talked with her privately. During the next week she thought about her situation, then told me of her realization that her in-laws were constantly telling her she was not good enough, that her lipstick or her dress were "all wrong," and that she compared poorly with a sister-in-law who "always looked stunning."

Physically she had drawn herself in to protect herself from the criticism. Her posture told this story. When she understood how the brain is programmed, she realized she was allowing this to happen to her. In her new enlightenment, she realized she was of value, with her own share of talents and abilities, and real contributions to make. She could learn how to express herself tastefully and accurately in her appearance.

As this woman got in tune with herself, she took command of her mind and her attitudes. She refused to be intimidated further. In just six weeks, she had grown into a new space with a totally different expression on her face and with lovely posture.

I believe that living life abundantly is an art, that "The arts that contribute to make life pleasant and beautiful are worthy of cultivation." The cultivation of these arts can work in harmony with the more solid and enduring qualities of honesty, sincerity, and virtue. Beauty, when it is in the heart as well as in the face, will produce a "beautiful life and noble practice."

I find art in every facet of life. The fruition of art in living is happiness and confidence. The qualities of nurturing, encouragement, and love are necessary tools of this art.

STAYING ALERT, STAYING ALIVE

As you go about the daily efforts of living, meeting the demands of your profession and/or family, it becomes easy to slip into a mental and emotional vacuum where you mindlessly react to survive. You can become so caught up in the lives of those around you that you lose sight of who you are, the influence you can have. You lose sight of the possibilities that can and should be yours.

Your values can be lived in every minute of the day, in how you speak to your husband or a coworker, in how you approach a daughter—how you hold her and care for her, how you talk to your son, how you treat the people you pass every day. I treasure this statement from a wise religious leader, David O. McKay. "To feel our capacities unfold and truth expanding our soul is one of life's most sublime experiences."

Start your inner beauty process by developing a value system that fortifies and nourishes your own sense of well-being. Base or determine how you want to look on this your value system.

When you live by what you believe in your deepest heart to be true, you have good self-esteem. When you do not live by what you believe, you have poor self-esteem and you do not like yourself.

Honor is power. The Beauty Code™ helps you declare your personal right of being and discover the power of the light in you. Add this power of light to your appear-

*You start **your inner beauty** process when you develop **values** that **fortify** and **nourish** your own sense of **well being*** ance to complete your own identity. Integrity within is the mooring of presence. It is a radiance beyond poise, composure, and refinement that communicates the core personality and character of the individual.

ACHIEVING BALANCE BETWEEN SELF AND OTHERS

I am convinced that it is in the importance of relationships of spouse, family, job, or love in service that life has its deepest meaning and reward. It is here that we have the perfect laboratory to hone our skills of character. Each relationship is an important element in our lives. I sense that an essential component for total beauty is that we never lose sight of the value, power, and influence of "I." You can't give from an empty cup, so fill it with knowledge, good character, noble acts. If the trappings of environment were suddenly taken from you, who are you? What would you be? What would you be about?

Ultimately, it is in community, not isolation that we satisfy the impulses of life

As we become more aware of our influence, we can become increasingly capable of filling a valued space in the lives of those who surround us. I see needs all around me. I've learned that the best food for my own soul is to help and lift (feed) someone else. It's a welcome smile when someone walks through the door. It's walking slowly, holding the hand of a grandchild learning to walk. My family, my friends need me to listen and to respond with encouragement. I can fill an important place just by meeting each moment with positive intent. I continue to grow in my ability to do this well.

Seeing people unfold from hopelessness into a conscious recognition of the incredible opportunities of life and contribution is one of the most fulfilling experiences of my life.

Ultimately, it is in community, not isolation that we satisfy the impulses of life. It is in relationships that we achieve security and guarantee our happiness, especially when we feel that we too have a vital, beautiful, contributing part of that community.

BE A FRIEND TO YOURSELF

Piece by piece, you are building a picture puzzle of your life. Recognize yourself. Speak to yourself. Love yourself. Know that you really are beautiful. Carefully choose the pieces that build the picture of this beautiful personal self. Develop integrity in yourself and you need never compromise your personal system of value. Living your life with this kind of wholeness will reawaken your spontaneity and confidence so those special people in your life will carry lingering reflections of your influence.

Lynn Deetz, image consultant, said, "It has been my greatest pleasure to experience the total Beauty Code System. As an image consultant for over six years, I've completed hundreds of consultations. Not until The Beauty Code™ did I find a color system that worked for everyone."

Lezlie Jones, homemaker, said, "It wasn't until I got into The Beauty Code™, that I learned how to become a beautiful woman. It helped me discover who I am."

Nicci Young, insurance agent, said, "I learned more about myself than anywhere else or ever before. I never believed I could be beautiful so I ignored cosmetic and beauty systems. I love the color system because it eliminated all the searching."

Sherry Jacobson, direct sales, said, "The Beauty Code™ has the best color system, an excellent makeup and skin care system so it's a total program. Based on truth and light, I still think it's the best there is. With The Beauty Code™, you can have a glamour look forever not just a one time shot. But it's better than a hard glamour look. The system and makeup bring out natural beauty—a softness. The system answers all the questions women have. It gives me more freedom."

The Beauty Code™ has given you the means of achieving balance and beauty in your appearance. Light, a principle of intelligence, truth, and life, can clarify and expand your signature self within—its values, its gifts, its dreams.

The Signature is yours. The Light is you.

Woman, the great **frontier** *of* **influence** *for* **all** mankind

When the feminist movement was demanding "equality," the implication was that we should be more like men. While I love and appreciate the gifts of men, I am a woman. Because I cherish my own gifts found only in woman-hood, I wrote this response.

WOMAN'S LAST FRONTIER OF SLAVERY

I believe the last frontier of slavery is woman.

Its shackles will not be removed by warring for rights of equality,

but won within the heart of each woman as she finds and firms

     the clarity of her vision,

     the sureness of her values.

     her integrity to what deep within her, she senses to be truth.

Finding fulfillment in developing her many facets.

Owning her right to choose,

Owning her right to speak quietly, confidently against any form of tyranny

     over the minds and souls of men--and her own soul

Secured by her virtue in the face of corrupt minds

Feeling the sparkle of light and fun and happiness give buoyancy to her spirit

     and those around her.

Recognizing the preciousness of each life, reverencing that life and the promise

     of its opportunity, she moves to bring abundance in happiness to the world.

Realizing the gentle results of nurturing, encouraging, and enveloping love–

     a love that expands, never diminishes, the light in another.

Knowing she has a mind and training it for contribution.

No longer vulnerable to externals,

     the majesty of her victory will come from within her.

Through her freedom, her understanding, and her influence of goodness

     . . . the yoke of all mankind can be broken.

Marilyn Starr Harris

Notes: 1) See article: Sensitivity of Men, *www.mybeautycode.com*

     2) "It is said that slavery has disappeared from European civilization. That is a mistake. It still exists. It preys now only upon woman. That is to say, upon grace, upon feebleness, upon beauty, upon maternity. This is not one of the least of man's shames." (David O. McKay, Brigham Young University, May 10, 1961.)

The **Signature** is *yours.*
The **Light** is *you!*

Marilyn Starr Harris has distilled years of one-on-one client experience plus her extensive research of the masters in science and art into her book, *Unlocking Your Beauty Code.* Author, image consultant and a successful business owner in the beauty world for over thirty-five years, she is the first in history to unlock the science behind personal color and style. Her knowledge replaces the beauty guessing game with scientific facts that can give you appearance mastery.

The Beauty Code™ introduces Marilyn's revolutionary new color system, *The Science of Personal Color™*, which shows how color relates to all people worldwide. With her discoveries, she has beauty down to a science—a science that makes looking attractive predictable. This predictability in results distinguishes this book from all other beauty systems and beauty books. Her clients talk of increased self-confidence, more personal fulfillment, and an increased ability to impact others.

Marilyn Starr Harris took advanced studies at the Sassoon School of Hair Design in London and Pivot Point International in Paris. Soon after receiving her cosmetologist license, she won first place for hair color in Utah's State Clairol Hair Contest, and third place for overall fashion look.

As a trained makeup artist with Merle Norman Cosmetics, Marilyn also learned pattern making and fitting from Marit Liset Kerr, a graduate of European couture houses. Her fabric stores offered custom design and sewing. Because of her broad training, she understands how colors, lines, textures, and expressions of personality speak signature messages to enhance beauty.

Her beauty-related businesses also include a cosmetic and lingerie shop for eight years, a makeover photography studio for five years, and a twelve-station hair and cosmetic studio for twelve years. She's acted as a fabric, clothing, jewelry, and accessory buyer for her businesses. She has put together four makeup lines for other companies. Today, Marilyn owns and advises her skin care company, MiraCell, Inc., as well as her beauty and cosmetics company, Beauty Innovations, which offers The Beauty Code™ system and cosmetics.

Marilyn believes in the beauty in every woman. Under her tutelage, many self-proclaimed wallflowers have transformed into attractive women. She advises women, men, U.S. senators, politicians, and career professionals with their appearance and mannerisms to help advance them in their life and career goals.

I express gratitude to my husband, Robert, my sweetheart, my friend, for his support mentally, emotionally, physically, and financially.

Gratitude and admiration go to our children Stuart, Linn, Lisa, Caren, Nathan, Kirt, Sara, and Weston for their encouragement and willingness to help me in my quest. For support, input and contribution to spouses, Laura Harris, Louis Martin, Keith and Katy Allred, Jeanette Harris, Susie Harris, Ted Cameron. To my sister Eileen Bayer, and my brothers and wives, Wayne, Lorraine, and Jeannie Thorpe, Allen and Elizabeth Thorpe, and Paul and Velda Thorpe.

I thank the many individuals who patiently helped and supported me in this endeavor: Julia Nuttall, a dream assistant and designer in all ways. Editor/writers Michael Clapier, Elizabeth Thorpe, Clifton Jolley, and LaVina Fielding Anderson for great advice and assistance. Designers, Shaun Knapp, Linda Maloy, Anthony Orme, and Marie Zamora for the perfecting details. For vision. Janet Switzer, without you, this book would still be a frustrated manuscript sitting on my office shelf. Bernie Dohrmann of CEO Space, now in 140 countries; Robert G. Allen, Mark Victor Hansen, and Richard Paul Evans who all helped me break the barriers of possibility. Harv Ecker, who helped collapse my wealth issues. Jay Abraham for teaching marketing reality.

Others who gave special help are:

Bob Gervich	Joy and Connie Conatser	Karla Gunderson
Richard and Darcus Gadd	Kay Givan	MarJean Pitcher
Carl Oliver	Antoine and Barbara Harris	ReNea Blair
Janet Seamons	Susy and John K.M. Olsen	Cleo Haroldson
Sheila Pickering	Eleanor Hall	Alice Buehner
Kathryn Greenwood	Monica and Sandy Jones	Rachael McComber
Georgia Bickmore	Ray Beckham	Carolyn Driggs
Kathy Frei	Joyce Francom	Alex Vaughn
Noleen and Paul Heaton	Lloyd and Mary Beth Pendleton	Theresa and Jay Taylor
Sherry Jacobson	Louise Knapp	Karen K. Christoffersen
Vickie Cooper	Vickie Tate	Elyse Harris
Jessica McGovern	Kaye Budge	Barbara Julius

acknowledgements

Beauty Resources

Find these items at www.mybeautycode.com

Beauty Code Color Discovery

- Discover your best colors—those colors that bring you into the balance of pure light—with this interactive online color tutorial.

- Using a photo of yourself which you send or email to us, we will show you color law and how it works for you to become more beautiful than you ever imagined.

Beauty Code Color Shopping Guide and Planner

- Convenient pocket- or purse-sized Color Shopping Guides to make shopping and decorating easier—for both women and men.

Perfect Match Cosmetic Collection

- Matched to *Your Beauty Code Color Collection*™

- See and choose from a variety of cosmetic cases designed for every need and budget at *www.mybeautycode.com*.

MiraCell® Skin Cosmeceuticals and Skin Care

- Protects and nourishes your skin with plant extracts fully compatible to your skin.

Clothing

- Color basics for each *Color Collection*. Jackets to express your moods and fill your needs.

Beauty Code CD's and DVD's

- Listen to the *Beauty Code* concepts, empowering principles and more while you drive or work, or you can watch on-screen while you rest.

Beauty Code™ *Insider Membership*

- Fashion Updates—clothing catalog maps to help you find clothes in your colors from current catalog offerings.

- Website specials for cosmetics, jewelry, and more.

- Discounts on products and services.

- First to know of and try new products.

- Monthly newsletter.

- Free reports and updates.

- Exclusive offers.

FUTURE MATERIALS

Beauty Code Figure Analysis and Style Guide

- As unique as the color program, figure analysis by computer introduces you to a new concept in measuring body proportions which unlocks the mystery of creating an exciting appearance. From over eighteen billion possible combinations of physical features, Your *Style Guide* teaches you your style code so you are the expert in choosing your most attractive necklines, collars, jackets, pants, sleeves, hairstyles, and accessories.

  Visit *www.mybeautycode.com* for full details.

Beauty Code DVD Presentations

- For each individual *Color Collection* with advanced information for extending wardrobes and ways to get more dramatic wardrobe and makeup effects beyond the space allowed in the book.

Beauty Code Career Track Seminars

- Seminars for beauty professionals including hair stylists, artists, clothing designers and manufacturers.

- *Beauty Code* brands licensing and retail merchandise

- A paint company, housewares, linens, and more.

FUTURE BOOKS

The Beauty Code™—Style; The Science of Personal Beauty—for Professionals, Designers and Manufacturers; The Code for Dynamic Appearances of Men

beauty resources

Credits *The Beauty Code*™

The Face on the Cover: This woman represents, to me, all women. She could be seen at any age of the earth among most any people. Our coloring may differ. Our features may differ. But as women, we are, and have always been, the breath and spirit of beauty to the world.

Front cover and spine: Design by Anthony Orme, design modifications by Julia Nuttall, Marie Zamora, Linda Maloy, and Christina McLauchlin.

Special thanks to Therese and Jay Taylor, owners of Renaissance Academie de Hair Design for hair and makeup. Staff: Mandy Humphrey, Jolaine Robinson. Beauty Code Staff. Photos by Stephen May.

Therese Taylor

Models: Pg x-xi: Collette Bingham. Pg xii: Claudia Queiroz. Pg xiv: Christina Strain. Pgs 16-17 Left to right, top to bottom: Kendra Stromberg, Tabitha Kaou, Lily Richards, Paige Andros, Taunya Budge, Eva Garlick, Andrea Evans. Pg 18: Kristen Rafajko. Pg 26: Melissa Ken. Pg 51: Tonya Budge, Holly Vaughn, Nicole Bunker, Claudia Queiroz, Lindsey Layton. Pg 57: top to bottom, Jen Weaver, Susan Nicholes, Nicole Bunker. Pg 86: Left middle, Taunya Budge, Left bottom, Becky Bradford, Right middle, Laura Bradshaw, Right bottom, Claudia Queiroz. Pg 90: Top row left to right: Sonja Shupe, Julie Nevers, Alicia Rose, Jen Weaver. Row Two: Kristina Urena, Paige Andros, Lexi Allred, Katy Allred. Row Three: 1) Christina Strain, 2) Alex Vaughn, 3) Susan Nicholes, 4) Holly Vaughn. Row Four: Brittany Davison, Nancy Lay. Pg 91: 2) Laura Bradshaw, 3) Stacy Gregerson, 4) Ashley Smith. Row Two: 2) Kendra Stromberg, 3) Andrea Richens, 4) Denise Woodward. Row Three: Kristen Chevier, Monica Jones, Melissa Ken. Row Four: 2) Tabitha Kauo Page 94: 1) Jen Weaver, 3) Holly Vaughn. Pg 95: 1) Tanya Budge, 3) Julie Nevers. Pg 96: Kelly Gummo, Becky Bradford, Julia Nuttall. Pg 97: 1) Andrea Evans, 3) Claudia Queiroz. Pg 98: Monica Jones, Laura Bradshaw. Pg 99: 3) Kristen Chevier. Pg 141: Lily Richards. Pg 147: Left to Right, Melissa Ken, Sandy Davis, Kelly Gummow, Kristina Urena, Laura Bradshaw, Tabitha Kauo. Pg 152: 2) Lindsay Layton [Jocelyn Brown]. Pg 153: Sandy Davis, Jeannie Hardin [Jessica Victor]. Pg 156: Susan Nichols. Pg 155: Kelly Gummow, Brittany Davison. Pg 156: Melissa Ken. Pg 157: Eva Garlick, Kristina Urena. Pg 158: Kendra Stromberg, Kaylee Black [Keisha Black]. Pg 159: Lisa McMillian, Nicole Bunker. Pg 160: Lily Richards, Denise Woodward. Pg 161: Kristen Chevier, Laura Bradshaw. Pg 162: Collette Bingham. Pg 163: Paige Andros, Lexi Allred. Pg 164: Ginger Harris. Pg 165: Andrea Richins, Erica Bowman. Pg 166: Becky Bradford. Pg 167: Claudia Queiroz, Taunya Budge. Pg 168: Lindsay Chapman, Ashley Allison. Pg 169: Christina Strain. Pg 170: Bekah Converse, Janine Converse. Pg 171: Jessica Thompson, Michelle Crandall. Pg 172: 2) Andrea Evans. Pg 173: Shelli Geilmann, Jessica Victor . Pg 174: Stacy Gregerson. Pg 175: Stephanie Hansen, Kehau Hao. Pg 178: Aspen Miller. Pg 179: Daria Jones, Emily La Bonte. Pg 180, Karli Keech, Haley Knight. Pg 181: 2) Nancy Lay. Pg 182: Jaci Latham, Jessica Latham. Pg 183: Holly Vaughn. Pg 184: Jen Weaver. Pg 185: Jessica Schroeder, Summer Murdock.

Pg 186: Rhonda Miller. Pg 187: Kristen Rafajko. Pg 188: Sonja Shupe, Kristen Taylor, 189: Ashley Smith, Tabatha Kauo. Pg 190: Rachel Otteson. Pg 191: Tammy Sandstrom. Pg 192: Alicia Rose, Ashlee Rose. Pg 199: Lexi Allred. Pg 200-201: Repeats Chart from Chapter 6. Pg 242: Sandy Davis. Pg 248: Becky Bradford. Pg 254: Brittany Davison. Pg 273: Susan Nichols, Eva Garlick.

Photos by Rick Nye; hair and makeup by Beauty Code staff: Tresia Korich, Janine Converse, Tristen Lewis, and Marilyn Starr Harris.

Models: Pg 16: Susie Harris, Julia Nuttall. Pg 17: Stephanie Hansen, Brenda Bird, Freda Rappleye. Pg 40: Jessica Reichman. Pg 51: Katy Allred. Pg 84: Gina Harris. Pg 86: Left 1) Katy Allred. Right 1) Carrie Ipson. Pg 90: Row Two 4) Katy Allred. Row Three 2) Alex Vaughn. Pg 91: Row Two 1) Carrie Ipson. Row Four: Brenda Bird. Pg 92: 2) Katy Allred.. Pg 93: 2) Sara Cameron. Pg 94: 3) Julia Nuttall. Pg 95 2) Susie Harris. Pg 96: 1) Susan Nicholes. Pg 97: 2) Carrie Ipson. Pg 108: Julia Nuttall. Pg 110: Katy Allred. Pg 152: Brenda Bird. Pg 162: Katy Allred. Pg. 166: Alex Vaughn. Pg 169: Sara Cameron. Pg 174: Adrienne Tedjamulin. Pg 175: Stephanie Hansen, Kehau Hao. Pg 176: Gina Harris, Aspen Miller. Pg 177: Susie Harris, Carrie Epson. Pg 181: Selina Weighill. Pg 183: Haven Miller. Pg 184: Letia Miller. Pg 186: Jessica Reichman. Pg 187: Julia Nuttall. Pg 190: 2)Carol Rutherford. Pg 191: 2) Freda Rappleye. Pg 244: Letia Miller. Pg 246: Adrienne Tedjamulin. Pg 250: Shelby Cameron. Pg 253: Sara Cameron. Pg 265: Stephanie Hansen. Pg 266: Marilyn Starr Harris. Pg 267: Marilyn and Robert Harris. Pg 273, Carrie Ipson.

Other Photographers and Stylists:
Photos by Andrea Gonzales; hair and makeup by Marilyn Starr Harris. Pg 96: 3) Janet Seamons. Pg 91, 97, and 164: 1)Kay Given. Pg 172: Karen Roberts. Pg 178: Shauna Coleman, Janet Seamons. Pg 193: Carrie Anderson, Caren Harris.

Photos by Mary Ann McCullom, Pretty Woman Studios, hair and makeup Sara Cameron, Michelle Wilcox. Pg 154: 1) Ann Burton. Pg 156: 1)Jodi. Pg 245: Penny F.

Photos by Shaun Knapp, Beauty Code staff. Becky Sampson. Pgs 229, 230, 232. Merrie Hudson. Pg 234-235, 238-239. Pg 273: Carol Rutherford, Jessie Olsen, Elizabeth Bateman

Photos from Family Albums. Pg 68: Carolyn Murdock, Karma Farrer, Sheila Pickering. Pg 90: Row 4, 3) Lisa Allred. Pg 267: Children of Marilyn and Robert Harris: Stuart Harris, Linn Martin, Lisa Allred, Caren Harris, Nathan Harris, Kirt Harris, Sara Cameron, Weston Harris.

Major book design: Julia Nuttall, Linda Maloy. Editing assistants: Carrie Ipson, Shaun Knapp. A special thanks to these individuals for their tireless dedication to this project.

Color Story Chapter 2: Marilyn Starr Harris.

Art: Ruth Brimhall Buckner

Color Wheel: Pg 86, Randall Smith Design, Katie Allred, Taunya Budge, Becky Bradford, Carrie Ipson, Laura Bradshaw, Claudio Queiroz.

Color Wheel, Pg 272, Marilyn Starr Harris, from top clockwise: Kay Givan, Carrie Ipson, Tammy Sandstrom, Laura Bradshaw, Janet Seamons, Kendra Stromberg, Andrea Evans, Brenda Bird, Letia Miller, Claudia Queiroz, Julia Nuttal, Jodie, Brittany Davison, Christina Strain, Alex Vaughn, Jeannie Harden, Taunya Budge, Holly Vaughn, Collette Bingham, Sandy Davis.

THE SCIENCE OF PERSONAL COLOR
ORIGINAL COLOR WHEEL
BY MARILYN STARR HARRIS

The Beauty Code Color Wheel addresses the four main elements of color: Hue - Temperature - Value - Intensity -

It shows how these elements of color relate to all people, blonde to brunette, warm and cool, those of intense or fragile color. People other than Caucasian fit into one of four color collections: Yellow Orange, Red Orange, Red Purple, and Blue Purple. Caucasian people fit into these four collections plus two more, Blue Green and Yellow Green.

This color wheel gives us a consistent and universal language to understand and communicate color accurately. It has application in all areas where color is an important factor including manufacturing and coordinations of clothing, cosmetics, hair coloring, home furnishings, vehicles and other. Developed by Marilyn Starr Harris for her Science of Personal Color.

Aquamarine
BlueGreen

Peridot
YellowGreen

Sapphire
BluePurple

Topaz
YellowOrange

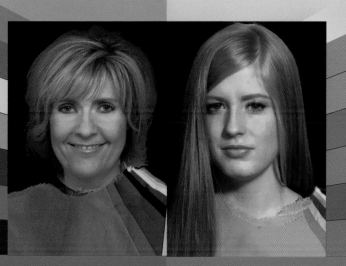

Ruby
RedPurple

Garnet
RedOrange

Aquamarine
BlueGreen

Sapphire
BluePurple

Ruby
RedPurple

Garnet
RedOrange

Topaz
YellowOrange

Peridot
YellowGreen